Link to Life

Epilepsy

Gary Johnstone
Series editor: Kevin Mulhern

B🌿XTREE

CENTRAL

ᴇer books in the *Link to Life* series:
..E.
Spinal Cord Injury

First published in Great Britain in 1995 by Boxtree Limited

Preface © Central Independent Television plc 1995
Text © Gary Johnstone 1995

The 'Link' Programmes are produced for Central Independent Television
by Coffers Bare Productions Limited

Cover design by Design 23
Typeset by SX Composing Ltd, Rayleigh, Essex
Printed and bound in the UK by Cox & Wyman for

Boxtree Limited
Broadwall House
21 Broadwall
London SE1 9PL

ISBN 1 85283 929 5
A CIP catalogue entry for this book is available from the British Library.

Contents

Preface

Ever since the 'Link' programme was first broadcast back in 1976, the philosophy behind it has been to avoid talking about different kinds of disability in isolation. I have always thought it was better to unite disabled people as a whole, rather than dividing them by their disabilities. Such categorization smacked too much of the doctors and disability professionals who dominate our lives and label us as 'blind', 'deaf', 'retarded' and so on. However, when Boxtree approached me and asked me to consider the idea of producing a series of books which took the approach of looking at individual disabilities, I was surprised to find that not only I, but most of the disabled people I spoke to, thought the time was right to do so.

The *Link to Life* series which emerged has proved a great success. The first two titles, which dealt with people with spinal cord injury, and with M.E., filled a vacuum which I had not realized existed. The response of readers has been to find those volumes informative and educational to the general public and at the same time offering a ray of hope and a focal point of comradeship to those people who have similar disabilities. It is as if, by emphasizing the individual experiences of disabled people, their shared experience is more heavily underlined.

For years disabled people's lives have been viewed as tragic and sad. What the 'Link' programme and the *Link to Life* books emphasize is that the problems we face are brought on by society's reaction to our disability rather than our disability itself. Disabled people are experts on their own disability: they live with it and manage it every day. What is most diffi-cult to deal with is the architectural and attitudinal barriers which are brilliantly laid out in this, the third book in the *Link to Life* series, a book that deals with epilepsy.

Over the years on 'Link', I have become accustomed to receiving letters which are often pleas for help from people with disabilities who have come face to face with the blatant and unthinking prejudice and discrimination which is still commonplace in day to day life. Much of this discrimination is disguised by the 'job's worth' school of bureaucracy, such as the cinema manager who swears that it is 'more than his job's worth' to admit some-body in a wheelchair into his cinema in case the fire officer should do a spot check on safety. This kind of discrimination and attitude is hard to overcome since the statute books are riddled with archaic pieces of legisla-tion which give the petty bureaucrat the opportunity to exclude you.

The most heart-rending examples of cruel and unthinking discrim-ination over the years have come from people who have epilepsy. The unfairness of these cases is emphasized by the fact that many people with epilepsy can conceal their disability, and are therefore only penalized when they are honest enough to inform people of it. I can recall a case of a woman who told an airline with whom she was planning to travel that she had epilepsy: she thought it was her responsibility to do so, even though her condition was completely under control. The airline insisted that she had to pay for a second ticket so that she would have a companion on board, the logic being that she might need someone to assist her if she were to have a seizure at the same time as an emergency evacuation of the plane was going on. The airline concerned was, I am pleased to say, roundly condemned by every other major airline, who pointed out that if they were to impose such a criterion for people with epilepsy, then every overweight male over forty years old should also have a travelling com-panion in case of heart attack during an emergency evacuation.

I also recall the heartbreaking story of a person who lost his job as a librarian when he revealed he had epilepsy. The logic of the local authority in this case was that he might have a seizure while standing on a ladder and injure somebody when he fell!

In the following pages, Gary Johnstone has done a superb job in dis-pelling the myths and misinformation about epilepsy. He has done this not by examining the scientific or medical research which is being carried on in the field, or by talking to the doctors and scientists who earn their living from epilepsy, but by allowing people with epilepsy to speak for themselves, to explain how they live their lives and overcome the real problems they face while sidestepping the problems created by other people. In these pages you will hear from, amongst others, a barrister, a teacher, a journalist and a businessman, all of whom have epilepsy. What is important is that they are speaking for themselves, a fundamental principle of the 'Link' television programme, and now the basis of Boxtree's *Link to Life* series.

Kevin Mulhern
March 1995

Introduction

This is not a textbook about epilepsy, and there's much in this book that goes against what many textbooks would recommend. For example, I decided after a while to stop taking medication for my epilepsy. I can't recommend that to anyone else. My epilepsy, my job, my lifestyle, my attitudes and beliefs make that possible. Most people with epilepsy find it simply impossible to live without constant medication. I have decided to go swimming regularly, but there is someone in this book who has decided swimming is too dangerous for her at the moment. There are organisations, with much more experience of the condition than I have, who make suggestions about what, in general, people with epilepsy should be careful about doing. However, they recommend behaviour and lifestyles that I refuse to be a party to. This is not because they are wrong, or extreme; it's just that I've made up my mind about what I can and can't do. I make no apology or claims for that. I'm not keen on making suggestions about what people should or shouldn't do, as suggestions often become rules.

What I do recommend knowing about are the experiences of other people with epilepsy. Sharing the thoughts, fears, hopes and joys of these people has given me the strength to make decisions about my life. No one can tell you what is right or wrong for you. In the end, it is up to you; but hearing how other people dealt with their, often similar, problems can be a real boost to making decisions for oneself.

That is what this book is: a collection of experiences of people with epilepsy. The people range from those with severe physical problems to those whose epilepsy is quite mild, but who have suffered problems in the way society has reacted to their condition. Their experiences are all quite different, yet they have much in common. It is finding the similarities in other people's experiences which I think is therapeutic.

I must stress that none of what is said by any of the participants in this book is approved, tested or endorsed by anyone else. What is right for me or for someone else may not work for you. There's a lot I disagree with in this book! Make your own mind up.

My one regret is that this book doesn't have enough space to fully tackle the shameful and continuing prejudice levelled at people with epilepsy. Children in schools and people at work are still harassed and misjudged because of their condition. There is still widespread ignorance of the many forms that epilepsy can take. Of course, things are getting better; but every month or so there are horror stories about children being told to look for another school because they have epilepsy. We shouldn't underestimate society's capacity to disregard our situation. I hope by reading the experiences of the people in this book, you will gain a confidence to tackle these situations better when you come across them yourself. I know from experience that it is all too easy to forgive the discriminator and accept the prejudice because we feel alone and overwhelmed by it. However, people with epilepsy have the right to be taken seriously.

Before hearing the experiences of others I was, frankly, confused about epilepsy. It seemed like a bewildering game of risk, with no real answers. Questions like 'How do you know whether to do this or do that?' kept entering my thoughts. Eventually, I made up my own mind about whether to do certain things or not, and gave up thinking about the whole issue. But I wasn't as happy with my condition as I thought I was. I had lapsed into a self-imposed isolation that I wasn't really aware of.

My epilepsy may have started when I was a young teenager. I used to get sudden attacks, possibly panic attacks, but what I now feel must have been epilepsy. It could be anywhere: at home, eating dinner, at school, reading a book, sitting on a bus. I felt a wave of darkness come over me, a wave of fear, almost like vertigo. I felt at the time as though I was being confronted by my own death; a black, infinite kind of panic. Then it would pass, but the residual emotion would stay with me usually for the rest of the day. Both I and my parents were very confused about this. I think they were quite worried about me for a while. I went through a period of very low confidence. I didn't want to do anything and took to my bed whenever I got back from school. A psychiatrist was suggested by my father but that seemed very threatening. After a while, probably by the time I was sixteen or seventeen, the attacks lessened, although I could never – and still can't – shake off the horrible memory of them.

The only other incident I can remember was much later, when I was about twenty-six. I'd been working for a presentations company, putting on various big conferences and shows around the world. We would often do a week in a big hotel and have to work long hours after each day's conference, preparing for the next day. Often we would end up working right through the night and the next day. On top of that, there was always – because of being in a group of people away from home and staying in a flash hotel – a lot of drinking at the client's expense. So generally, the whole trip would be utterly exhausting. It wasn't uncommon to wake up and wonder where the hell I was. But one day, while staying in Monte Carlo, having gone to bed in the afternoon after an 'all-nighter', I woke up. I had a splitting headache and for at least ten minutes not only did I not know where I was, but I also didn't know who I was. I got up and looked in the bathroom mirror, but that only made me feel worse. I looked in my wardrobe and didn't recognize the clothes. I was feeling very woozy, but catching sight of a dinner suit made me start to remember that I was supposed to be going to work at a cabaret that evening. I got dressed, and slowly things came back to me. I never forgot that experience and at first put it down simply to exhaustion. Later, I found it was very similar to subsequent attacks which were diagnosed as epilepsy.

A few years later, when I was twenty-nine, two things happened on the same day that led to that diagnosis. By this time I was working in video production as a freelance director. I was quite a workaholic and was always getting very wound up by my job. That day, I had just started working for a new company. A group of us went to the pub for lunch. Meeting new people makes me a bit tense, so I wasn't very relaxed. I didn't drink any alcohol and had an ordinary lunch. We were chatting away, when someone asked me if we were going to be shooting on film or video. The word 'video' just stuck in my head. It was like it got lodged in there and wouldn't move. If the processing of words was like a pipe, then 'video' blocked the pipe. I kept repeating it over in my head. And people were looking at me wondering why I hadn't replied. I tried to talk, but all I could say was 'Video, video?' I knew that I knew the word. It wasn't like *not* being able to remember a word that you know and being cross that you couldn't call it up. The word was there, but I couldn't 'crunch' it. It was a most unpleasant feeling, as if my brain was breaking down. I felt very strange for about ten minutes and decided to have a walk around in the fresh air. I tried to put the feeling to the back of my mind and went back to work.

Otherwise, it was a normal day. I went home, went out to meet friends for a drink, and came home about 9.30pm. My girlfriend and I had a bowl of pasta and went to bed. I woke up in the middle of the night to find two ambulance drivers in my bedroom and my girlfriend looking petrified. I was totally confused. One of the ambulance drivers was asking me my name and I didn't know it. I started to cry. My heart was going like a rocket and I hurt across the chest. At first I thought I'd had a heart attack and started getting quite agitated. They assured me I hadn't. I was asking what had happened. Apparently, I'd been arching my back, con-vulsing, going rigid and making a weird groaning sound for about ten minutes, and then I'd passed out. I don't remember any of this.

They put me in the ambulance and took us off to the hospital which was quite a long way away. I don't remember much except sitting in casualty, in the waiting area. A doctor came up and the first thing he asked was whether I had been taking drugs! I said no, and my girlfriend explained what had happened. The doctor looked quite cross and said, 'You've had some sort of fit. Go and see your GP in the morning.' And with that he left. I was shocked, but too shattered to say anything. There I was sitting in a dressing gown, at five o'clock in the morning, my girl-friend in bits, and both of us wondering how to get home. I thought we had been in casualty for about fifteen minutes before I was seen, but ap-parently we had been there for five hours.

The next day I had the mother of all headaches, and it lasted for two days. I phoned in to work sick. I was honest with them and they were very supportive about it. Somehow I got to the doctor and he said I'd better see a specialist because it sounded like epilepsy. I remember thinking, at the time, 'Well, that isn't a problem'. I had a degree in psychology, so I knew what it was and I'd shared a flat with a couple of people who had it. But really, I was putting a brave face on it. I think, looking back, that I was quite freaked out by the whole process.

The business of seeing the consultant and having tests was pretty sur-real. It was like being in someone else's life. It felt like a film happening in front of my eyes. The hospital situation was pretty sad: neurological departments full of people with really bad head injuries, waiting for ages to be seen. I do remember thinking, though, 'By God, I'm getting my National Insurance money's worth!'

They rolled out all their best toys for me. I had an EEG – an electroencephalograph. Lots of electrodes are stuck to your scalp to measure your brain waves. The operator shows you all sorts of stimuli – lights and shapes, etc. – to try and provoke an abnormal brain pattern. I kept hoping I would have one, just so there would be some physical evidence; so I could say to them and the people around me – 'See, I'm not imagining it!' I think some of my friends thought I was exaggerating.

I also had a scan. They injected me with about a pint of blue stuff and I lay on a bed while lots of hi-tech machinery rotated around me. The fact that they all sat in another room wearing lead lined coats amused me. Despite all these gizmos, the experience was mainly boring and very frustrating. There never seemed anyone who was willing to tell me anything. As I was leaving the scan I looked in the control room. They were all laughing and chatting about something. I called in, 'Find anything, then?' They looked at me as though I had interrupted their fun. One of them said, 'We'll be passing the results on to your consultant.' That was the same sort of 'Who knows?' response I got from pretty much everyone.

Two weeks passed and I had a couple more 'funny-word' experiences. Eventually, I had a proper meeting with the consultant, and she told me I was epileptic. Nothing in the tests showed anything abnormal, (which is common) but the symptoms were pretty conclusive. She explained that everyone has an 'epileptic threshold', and that mine was low. She said I would have to take pills: anti-convulsants. She gave me a few leaflets, and a red card from the British Epilepsy Association. On it were some guidelines for how to live, now I had epilepsy. Some of the ones I can remember were don't have too deep a bath, don't lock the bathroom door, don't stand too close to the edge of train platforms or the road at bus stops. I had inch-deep baths for a while, but gave that up after a bit. I started locking the bathroom door again. I stopped skulking around the back of Tube platforms. The consultant had suggested I control my drinking, because it might affect the efficacy of the pills. That didn't last long.

The first six months were a funny period, though. I liked the idea of getting pills – I started taking Tegretol. I thought they might calm me down a little. I vaguely thought they might make me less of an intolerant bastard to everyone around me. What they did do – and I slowly came to resent it – was make my thinking dull. I felt that the edge had been taken off my brain-power, but had left my personality intact. That, to me, interfered with work. When I went back to the hospital for a three-month check-up, I saw a different doctor who said he didn't think the pills could be doing that. I've since read that they can make you feel drowsy and muddled. I was just bundled out of his office, and thought 'Why haven't I been more assertive about this?' Looking back, I must have been quite intimidated by it all.

It was hard to work out how my life should be after that diagnosis. I lost my driving licence which became a real pain. The leaflets I had been given didn't inspire me to call any of the associations. I tried to talk to an old friend who had epilepsy, but his attitude was 'It's no big deal'. So I guess I just settled down into doing as I had done before. I cycled everywhere, went swimming, drank and worked like crazy. It was only when people asked if I was 'allowed' to do all these things that I got confused. I worked out that it was all about risk. I decided that I was quite a high risk-taker and that was why I did all these things. I was really frustrated by the effect the pills had on my mental sharpness, so one day, after forgetting to take them, I just decided to stop taking them and see what happened. I also stopping drinking alcohol as a way of meeting the condition half-way.

A couple of months later I went back for a check-up. It was now about a year and a half since the original diagnosis. This time, I saw a young guy, about my own age. He said to see how things went. He also read me most of my notes. Apparently, according to the scan, I do have a scar on my left temporal lobe. It has helped to know that. Why I wasn't told before, I don't know. But to know about it really helped me make sense of what was, before, a lot of 'ifs' and 'possiblys'.

I guess I would have stayed in that state – 'Well, I've got something to do with epilepsy, but I'm not sure what it means and what the future of it is' – if not for getting involved in a television programme about epilepsy. I met loads of people with epilepsy. The experience of hearing so many stories was both a revelation and a relief.

First, with regard to my own condition, everything at last gelled. Other people with bumps or scars on their left temporal lobes had many of the same symptoms. The problems with words, the weird death-like feelings and the effects of a big fit were not just peculiar to me: many people had them. So I wasn't bonkers after all. Just about everyone agreed that stress played a part, which hadn't been made clear to me by the medics. I also felt I could sum up my situation at last and come to terms with it. I have mild epilepsy. I don't take medication. Tonic-clonic fits seem to happen at night when I am run down. I accept that. My word problems happen now and again. I know when they will and I don't care if people think I'm a bit loopy at the time: I have epilepsy, and if they can't cope with that then it's their problem. Sometimes I think it's going to get worse, and I accept that if it does medication may be necessary.

What really changed my attitude to the condition was hearing about how many people had been discriminated against at school and work, and were suffering more from people's attitudes than the actual epilepsy! The social effect of the condition was worse than the physical one. I've met people in residential care whose epilepsy seems to be no worse than mine but who are incapable of going to the shops on their own. Parents', teachers' and society's attitudes have so badly undercut their confidence that they are utterly disabled. No amount of medical research is going to make those people any better. I have escaped that minefield by being diagnosed at a later age. But the idea that I could be discriminated against at work or whatever really made me sit up and think.

The range of discrimination starts from me and my 'So, what if I've got away lightly; I can stand up for myself' approach, and extends all the way to people who have been made dysfunctional by society. If I, and everyone else whose epilepsy is in control, glide through life, picking and choosing where and when to disclose our epilepsy, pretending we're normal and charming people out of their fears about it, then where does that leave the others? Yet if I say I'm disabled, people think I'm mad. But now I say it in the same way people have said 'I'm Gay and Proud', and 'I'm Black and Proud'.

What I've come to believe is that disability isn't something to be frightened and ashamed of, but something to be fought for. We have a right to be the way we are and not to be put down for it. Because to me, and many others, disability isn't so much defined by physical differences but by society's reactions to those differences. I'm not suggesting that I, or anyone else whose epilepsy is under control, are having the same problems as the person who has three tonic-clonic seizures a day, or for that matter the person who is in a wheelchair, or who has cerebral palsy. But we do all share, to varying degrees, discrimination based on society's fears and ignorance. By being 'out' about my disability, hopefully I'll be part of a ground swell against that.

People sometimes get unhappy at my use of the word 'epileptic'. The politically correct way is to say 'person with epilepsy'. That way you are stressing they are people first and have epilepsy second. This I understand, but I also quite like giving it to people in the face. 'I'm epileptic' is aggressive. Sometimes you need that. I might be wrong. But where has the appease and educate approach got us? Where did it get Neville Chamberlain? All rights movements – gay, black or women's – have had to get tough and bolshie. Sometimes the prejudice just won't go away any other way.

There is, of course, another way to eliminate the discrimination and prejudice against epilepsy, which is to cure us all. Or, until that day comes, at least control our conditions nearly all the time. That way we can all say we are normal and there will be no discrimination. Many people see this as the best approach and are living individual versions of it today: take your pills and tell no one. I understand this approach. Who wants to put themselves up for potential discrimination? But I can't be part of it. Maybe I'm lucky because I was diagnosed late. I haven't had thirty years of being called 'epi'. But I still believe hiding will backfire on itself. You might save yourself, but some other little kid who can't hide will get picked on.

To deny your condition perpetuates a myth that there is such a thing as 'normal', and it tacitly accepts discrimination. It is in effect exonerating the discriminator and attempting to eradicate the object of their fears. I feel that society would be a much better place to live if people with all disabilities, including epilepsy, were accepted as useful members of our race with, like everyone, their own unique perspective on life and their active part to play in it. That to me is progress. God help us the day the world is completely made up of normal people. What a bore!

Gary Johnstone

Suzie Castle

Suzie Castle is a barrister and has had epilepsy since she was born.

I had my first fit when I was six weeks old. My parents weren't told I was epileptic; they were told I had febrile convulsions. I went on being told I had febrile convulsions until I was in my mid-teens, and basically, that they were something you grow out of. My little sister had them and grew out of them. I think my brother had them and grew out of them. They kept saying, 'when you hit puberty they'll stop', and I hit puberty and they didn't. In fact I had more. When I was about fifteen, eventually the local paediatric clinic said, 'Well actually, you are epileptic'. And it was a sentence. Suddenly I was something else. Up until then I'd been an ordinary person who had febrile convulsions, which was a bit rough occasionally, but when I was epileptic I felt I was categorized, labelled.

When I was very young, I don't remember how my parents reacted but during my childhood my parents were always very supportive. They were never anything else; they were used to it. They started off feeding me phenobarbitone crushed into jam to make me swallow it when I was a child, so by the time I was fifteen, epilepsy was just a regular part of our life. They'd had me carried home by boyfriends and rung up by the school, and over the years they'd picked me up and dusted me off on many occasions, and never been anything but totally supportive.

There was no panic about being diagnosed finally as epileptic. It was a totally private thing, I didn't discuss it with them; I didn't discuss it with the doctor. But a little bit of me didn't like the idea that I was epileptic. First of all, there was the fact that I was 'epileptic', a term which for me had the wrong connotations. And secondly, it felt like a life sentence, because until then it had always been something I was going to grow out of, and suddenly it was something I was always going to have, and that felt different.

I wasn't frightened at that point. I think depressed would be more like it. I suppose with hindsight I thought less of myself in consequence, although that's not how I thought about it at the time. I really didn't discuss it with anyone. I completely internalized the epilepsy itself. I had coped with the febrile convulsions as a child. They had caused me problems now and then but they were part of my life and I just dealt with them. But actually being told I was never going to grow out of it hit me quite hard at the time.

Even so my parents had given me such supreme self confidence in some ways that it never occurred to me that it was going to affect my life seriously. Some people said things like, 'Well, I don't know if you ought to go to university and live in a flat', but my parents always said, 'You go to university, you get a flat'. In fact, when I went to university, and I was staying in my first hall of residence I didn't tell anybody I was epileptic. I was in the house and I had a fit. I hadn't been there very long and I remember coming round and the matron saying to me, 'Why didn't you tell us?' The reason was that it hadn't occurred to me because I didn't think of myself as epileptic. It was only a couple of years after I'd been told, but I'd got back into the way of thinking of myself as me first and not epileptic. Epilepsy was just incidental. I didn't breeze into the house when I first moved in and say, 'Oh, and by the way, I'm epileptic.' I didn't tell them, but I didn't not tell them out of shame. I just didn't tell them because I didn't think it was important. After meeting other people with epilepsy and seeing how some people's lives have been so clearly dominated by being epileptic, I think now I was very lucky.

After I was diagnosed my behaviour probably did change somewhat. I didn't do less; quite the opposite. When I was a teenager in the north of Scotland, I and all my friends were furiously trying to prove that we weren't simple middle class girls, that we were more sophisticated than we really were. We were all trying to be much tougher, more grown up and more worldly-wise than we really were, and I don't think the epilepsy stopped me playing my part in that. But in later years – my late teens and early twenties – probably the one thing that showed my reaction to the epilepsy was a determination to do more, drink more, live more, be wilder and tougher than I might have been if I hadn't felt the need to prove something. I was definitely proving something to myself at that stage.

My experience of the medical profession was mixed. We used to go to the local hospital, the Dunbar, a couple of miles out of Thurso, which looked like a fairy castle. All the doctors I met when I was young were paternalistic, patronising, very nice and I just assumed that was the way it was. At the time I had no criticism at all of the way I was treated by the medical profession, partly because I didn't have the information or the confidence to be critical. I've no reason to assume that they were anything less than perfectly competent.

My first run in with the medical profession was when I went on the pill. I told my doctor I was epileptic which indeed she knew, and she put me on the pill nonetheless, and happily, nothing happened. I didn't get pregnant, but some time later at university my doctor showed me a little magic chart and said, 'Well, you can't have told your GP that you were taking these drugs because they interact with the kind of pill that you're on to reduce the medical efficacy of both'. So both the pill and the other drugs were less efficient. I wasn't terribly impressed by that, I have to say.

The next problem, I think, was when I changed drugs. I changed from phenobarbitone which was a very old-fashioned drug by then to a more modern drug, and I had a string of fits. I went back to the hospital in Edinburgh and said 'By the way, I've had three fits. What's happening? These drugs aren't working.' They said, 'Oh, don't worry. That's to be expected.' By that time I was well over eighteen but they didn't bother to tell me that the changeover of drugs would increase the risk of my having fits. Had they told me, I might have been in two minds about the changeover. Even if I'd agreed to the changeover, I would have liked to have known in advance, but they didn't credit me with that amount of intelligence, and they didn't bother to tell me.

Now I have a very nice consultant who I only go and see whenever something goes wrong. His parting shot to me normally is, 'Give me a ring in six months time.' He's delightful. I was moved from one sort of drug to another which now suits me very well. I was moved sensibly, but there was one last problem. Apparently the kind of drug I'm on now has a toxic level. It has to be at a perfect level in your blood stream to be efficient, but basically the only way of knowing when the level is too high, if you don't go in to have lots of blood tests, is when it becomes toxic. When that happens you start to experience symptoms like double vision, black spots, nausea and all sorts of odd feelings. Again, nobody actually told me in detail what to expect. It does say on the wrapper that if you experience any of these things to tell your GP immediately, but not having been told what was likely to happen, when I did get toxic poisoning I didn't know what I'd got.

The first time I was in a car, being driven a long way by a friend of mine for a court hearing. I felt really odd. I kept having double vision and I thought I must stop drinking. I didn't associate it with the tablets at all. The next day I went to Hitchin County Court and at nine in the morning on the train, my legs went from under me. I got up to walk from the carriage to the door into the station and collapsed. I think everyone thought I was drunk because like all good British people they backed off and didn't offer me a hand. I got off the train by moving from handrail to handrail, and collapsed again. I couldn't walk and the station master or the porter ordered me a taxi which took me to the court. The taxi driver put me on his arm to get me into the court. I got into the court and fortunately, the judge knew who I was – I'd appeared there a lot – and I got a message to him. I burst into tears; it was incredible. I couldn't understand what was happening to me.

I rang my GP who was a marvellous woman but didn't know about the tablets. It wasn't her responsibility but she looked it all up in Mimms (a doctors' drug guide) and said, 'What's happened is that you're over the limit; you've got a toxic overdose. Don't take any more and it will pass, and go and see your consultant.' She was right and it did pass, and the judge heard me sitting down, and made a remark about people being unwell in court. As far as I can remember, I won.

Since then it's been fine so I now have a good level and I haven't had a fit, touch wood, for just over a year. Hopefully, I can get a driving licence soon. In fact, I'm terrified to go and get the forms in case I somehow precipitate some terrible event.

For a while, my fits varied between two or three a year. They're stress related. With me, it usually takes a mixture of things. For example any one of these things won't bring a fit on by itself but if I forget a pill, get terribly stressed, terribly tired, have PMT, if I'm going down with flu or something, or getting over it, anything which renders me slightly constitutionally less strong goes towards making me have a fit. The two things that bring it on now are if I'm very tired, or if I'm very stressed. The one thing I shouldn't do in my job – and I do sometimes – is to drive myself too hard and say, 'I've got to do this; I must'. I stay up until four in the morning working or something and then get up again three hours later and go to court, and it can have the wrong effect. The last time I had a fit was one of those. I had worked for about three days flat out and not slept properly. I got up at some ungodly hour, four or five in the morning, and worked flat out, went to court and at the door of the court, just as this extremely stressful trial was about to start, keeled over. Result: end of the trial for a week or two. This means I have to control stress; I have to not let myself get completely stressed out.

Of course, you can't legislate against getting frightened, and in this job as you go on doing things that are more difficult, as you get more senior, you go on being made nervous by them. Other people may not but I certainly do. Every time I do something the next stage up in difficulty, I worry terribly and I get stressed. Having epilepsy doesn't feed into that stress. When I'm feeling worried about a case the possibility that I will keel over is probably the least of my worries, although it is there. The trial I've just finished was, in fact, the same trial where I keeled over before. For all sorts of other reasons it didn't start until much later, not because of my epilepsy. But as it was due to start again, I was feeling extremely stressed out about it, for different reasons this time, and it did cross my mind that I might have a fit. It also crossed my mind in the next breath that it really wouldn't do me, my client or my career very much good if I passed out a second time over the same trial!

The legal profession has been marvellous about my epilepsy. I'm open about it. I have to be open about it; I couldn't conceal it. Pupillage is a very stressful time for anybody coming to the bar because you have to prove yourself all the time and not get anything wrong, ever – at least that's how you feel when you are a pupil. When I was in pupillage I had two or three fits in a short space of time. I was quietly taken aside and it was suggested to me, by somebody with the best of intentions, that perhaps I should try and go into something more clerical and less stressful. That person suggested they might know somebody in the Lord Chancellor's department and would I like to be steered in that direction because I plainly wasn't cut out for the bar because I couldn't handle the stress. I reacted to this fairly ungraciously and I'm still here.

Nowadays, perhaps because I'm older and I'm more used to dealing with it and am more confident about my ability at the bar, it's much less of an issue. It hardly ever comes up. Whenever it has I've been treated with the utmost courtesy and support by courts and the court staff, but they still don't really know how to react to it. They're sort of ill-informed, I find, when epilepsy comes up.

The first time I had to cross-examine an armed robber, I was a bit nervous about it. I was prosecuting an armed robbery, which for me then was a fairly heavy case. If you're prosecuting a case, the acid-test moment is when you get to cross-examine the defendant (if they give evidence) because it can make all the difference, one way or the other, on how that particular piece of the case goes, so it's important. Before lunch I knew that I was going to have to cross-examine an armed robber who was actually very nice!

During my lunch-time I was furiously writing questions with one hand and eating a sandwich with the other, feeling iller and iller. So I said to my opposite number, a very nice man, 'By the way, I'm epileptic and not feeling awfully good. If I suddenly ask the judge for an adjournment it means I'm going to have a fit.' This was because if you ask the judge for an adjournment in the middle of the trial his first reaction is going to be, 'Why, what's the matter?' People don't just get up and chuck the jury into the jury room and stop proceedings. So my opposite number said, 'Okay'.

In the criminal court, everybody is robed up. The judge and barristers are wearing wigs, and if you've got a proper judge he'll be wearing a red and purple gown. Everybody is wearing bands (a stiff collar with white tags, like an eighteenth century vicar). It's all very serious, and nobody takes their wigs off, ever! In the summer, if it's 90 degrees and the air conditioning isn't working the judge may say 'wigs off', but in normal circumstances nobody takes them off, and if they do it means it's a serious emergency.

On this occasion, after lunch, I got to my seat because I knew I was going to have a fit and said, 'I'm terribly sorry, but would your honour rise?' He was just about to ask why when my opposite number leapt to his feet, took his wig off and said, 'Your honour should rise'. The judge looked at him and just went. He was gone! I got to the robing room before I had a fit and the trial resumed the next morning. So that was a dramatic response.

More often, I manage to convey without any major drama that I am not feeling very well, go away and have it quietly, or lie down. The courts have always been brilliant about that.

There have been two reactions of the bar which are more recent. A month or two ago, I was again in a long case. It had been going on for a week or two, and the judge knew me in a sense: if you're doing work in front of somebody every day, they get to know you a bit. At the end of the first week I knew that I was at risk. I was feeling really tired – it might have been my period – and I thought there was a risk that I was going to have a fit, so I explained to the judge in the absence of the jury first thing in the morning that I was epileptic and that there was this possibility. His reaction during the course of the trial and during the rest of the day, was to be very sympathetic almost to a fault. I'm sure if I'd sneezed he'd have given me an adjournment. But his reaction in the absence of the jury was to say to me, 'Don't embarrass yourself, Miss Castle'. I thought, I'm not embarrassed, or I shouldn't be, and if I am embarrassed it's only because I anticipate a negative reaction. I didn't like the comment although I'm sure it was kindly meant.

The only other way I come across this ignorance – and I come across it quite a lot – is when I do family work, and I do a lot of family work now. I regularly come across cases in which it is suggested that because of somebody's epilepsy they should not be made 'ousted'. For example, in an application for an 'ouster' injunction, which is when a marriage is breaking down, the courts have power to exclude one of the couple from the matrimonial home, because of violence or something similar. I have seen people suggest or argue that because a man is epileptic, he should not be excluded. I tend to think, although I have every sympathy with anybody who is on the receiving end of that sort of injunction, that if epilepsy is controlled and dealt with as it is in the vast majority of cases, then it's a bad reason for not making somebody homeless.

Similarly, I have seen it used in children's cases. On more than one occasion it has come up, and people have said the father or mother of these children is epileptic and therefore cannot look after them. 'What would happen if they were alone and she had a fit?' (That takes me back to the 'You can't live in a flat because what would happen if you were alone and you had a fit.') I think it's a terrible argument. If epilepsy is under control, then if somebody is about to have a fit in most cases they will have sufficient warning to do something about it. A child over the age of three or four can pick up the phone and dial 999 if necessary. Epilepsy is not a reason for taking a child away from either parent. I'm sorry to say the argument is nevertheless used, but I'm pleased to say that I've never seen it advanced successfully. On the occasions when I've seen it used, judges have dismissed it and the reaction has been civilized, which is an acknowledgement of the level of changing attitude towards epilepsy. Even so, the suggestion that epilepsy debilitates parents in some way is a reflection of the fact that society's attitudes are not yet where they ought to be. The legal profession, however, on the whole, is remarkably aware; it's really not bad. These days, getting a pupilage is very difficult. When I applied I can't remember whether I put epilepsy on my curriculum vitae, but I probably didn't. In those days they didn't send out forms, you just sent in a CV saying 'I came top in English in 1963', or whatever. Nowadays, chambers send out forms and the forms will probably be along the same lines as the ones produced by the major multinational companies, which means that they will probably have on them a question about epilepsy, diabetes and that sort of thing. Because I wasn't asked I didn't tell. I don't think I told anybody that I had epilepsy before I started pupilage because it occurred to me that they might hold it against me. I've always worked on the basis that when you know somebody and they know you, but not you as an epileptic person, I will tell them. I've always worked on the basis of complete openness once I know somebody, but never telling anyone if I can avoid it in advance of that, for fear of the reaction.

It has been suggested there should be a law against putting that kind of question on an application form. As a matter of law, I've never considered it. As a matter of policy it strikes me as a very good idea because it's not a relevant question, unless you're doing something like working with fast-moving machinery without guards or flying an aeroplane: somewhere where you would be a danger to yourself, or where you would be a danger to other people. But leaving those aside – and that must be all of 2 per cent of the job market – any other situation is completely irrelevant.

If you are epileptic and you have a fit, providing that the people that you are dealing with react in a civilized manner, it doesn't matter. It's a minor detail. People don't put on forms, do you suffer from migraines? backache? bad period pains? Do you regularly get terrible colds? Are you an alcoholic? In my working life now I probably lose, if anything, a couple of days a year, if that, and there is no reason why it should be of any relevance at all. Obviously it depends to some extent on the job, and to some extent upon how uncontrolled the epilepsy is. Certainly, if I had continued to have stress-related fits every time I walked through a court, then I wouldn't have been able to continue this career. But I didn't, and you have to push yourself to find out and you have to be allowed to push yourself to find out.

What does annoy me is the financial institutions that make a killing out of my condition. I pay pensions, life insurance policies, bank loans, and they load my premium because I'm epileptic, as if in some way this is going to have some effect. Somebody, somewhere, has a table that says if you are epileptic it is more likely that you will drop dead, walk under a bus or develop some terminal illness. I know that in my particular case, as far as I can tell – and I'm sure I have as good an idea as the average insurance company – there are no particular reasons related to my health or my lifestyle that mean I should be a bad risk compared to somebody else. I go on paying the premiums because I don't have any choice, but it does make me cross.

Going back to the physical side of epilepsy, when I've had a fit I feel immediately awful, completely out of touch. The most awful feeling is not knowing. You always wonder if this time your brain is damaged. When you come round you feel very groggy and people dealing with you, such as paramedics, ask you questions like 'What is your name, address?' The most frightening feeling in the world is when somebody asks me what my name is and I don't know. I have never forgotten sitting in an ambulance being driven in the wrong direction away from my flat, about 200 yards away, with an ambulance man asking very nicely, 'Where do you live Susan?' I couldn't remember. I knew I was somewhere nearby and then gradually, as we moved away, I realized it was somewhere near but I couldn't tell him. It was terrifying. You always think the fog isn't going to clear, because you know that there is always a possibility of brain damage, and it's horrible. You also have a splitting headache at least for the rest of the day. Usually, in my case, it lasts for about forty eight hours, and of course your tongue hurts like hell because you've bitten it. You just feel pole-axed for about forty-eight hours, but the really scary bit is the time it takes for you – and it varies from fit to fit and person to person – to regather your personality and to get your memory back in order.

Until your memory works you are not a person because you can't communicate, so you can't identify yourself.

Usually, if you have a fit somewhere in public, people call an ambulance. They have no idea what to do and they think you could be dying. If I have a fit, on most occasions I know beforehand I'm going to have one. I have enough time to lie down, loosen my clothes, take my contact lenses out and tell somebody. My last words are always 'Don't call an ambulance. It's all right, just stay with me,' and I usually come round in an ambulance half an hour later. Although they're getting better, the courts now know not to call ambulances in the vast majority of cases, and my friends all know not to call an ambulance. Usually I manage to say to them, 'Call X', and some unfortunate friend or boyfriend will be dragged out of a meeting and sent off to wherever I am. I still tend to get taken to hospital, which is unfortunate because by the time I arrive there, usually I'm feeling better; not great, but I can walk and I'm beginning to make sense. I feel an absolute fool because they produce a stretcher or wheelchair and they put a little blanket over my knee and wheel me in on the basis that I must be really ill because they've been called.

I suppose that because I have tonic-clonic fits, they are quite unpleasant when they happen. They're not very pretty and, of course, if you go into stasis, where the fit does not stop, and you need hospital treatment, it can be serious. Things are getting better, I encounter now a much higher level of awareness, amongst people who have had medical training, not professional ambulance men but the people who do or don't call an ambulance. I think maybe the Lord Chancellor's department has been training people but I seem to be getting a higher, more informed response now than I was when I first started off going to courts years ago.

If I say I'm epileptic, I don't generally get bad reactions from the public any more. I still get a response which is a slight surprise. People who don't know anyone who is epileptic are still surprised, at the very least, that I've said I am. I haven't heard a particularly ignorant response to epilepsy for some time, but it may just be that I move in circles now where people are too civilized to actually say something negative, even if they think it.

When I was younger I got ill-informed reactions to epilepsy. At school, there was a teacher who told my mother when she discovered I was epileptic, 'There, there, who would have thought it? Such a bonny, intelligent-seeming child.' I had other problems at school, such as being short, overweight, wearing spectacles and being English in a Scottish school and all sorts of other things, but as well I did get a bit of name-calling about epilepsy.

The most excruciating experience I can remember was passing out at the age of about 12 or 13 in the swimming pool and being dragged out by my school mistress. She took me into a tiny cubicle and dressed me. She should have sat me on the bench until I felt better, but instead she tried, doubtless for my personal dignity – and it was good of her – to get me dressed. I was still incredibly groggy and not making sense, and the rest of the class were gathered outside the cubicle giggling and listening. It was all very exciting for them, listening to my teacher saying things to me like, 'Come along, Susan, put your left foot through this left hole,' trying to get me to put my pants on. Everybody else thought it was hysterical, for ages afterwards. There was a tendency, at least in primary school to think that there was something odd about me. Children are so appalling.

We had a boy in our class at school who also suffered from epilepsy, but in a much less controlled version than mine. He was regarded by the class as the class idiot, and I'm sorry to say that as an ill-informed child I ascribed to this view as well. I didn't understand it, but by primary seven he couldn't write his own name and he was completely ostracized. He was then taken away, as he should have been a long time before, to a school where they could cope with epilepsy. The last time I heard from my mother I was enormously pleased to hear that he'd gone to university. I don't know what became of him subsequently, but at our school because nobody knew how to deal with him, he was the butt, treated like the village idiot. And he can't have been the village idiot at all. If he hadn't eventually been sent to a school where people acknowledged that he wasn't stupid, I don't know what he'd be doing now: nothing I imagine.

If a cure for epilepsy came along I'd be delighted. For one thing, I'd like to start a family, and I'm a little bit nervous about it, for two reasons. One is that there is an increased chance – it's increased threefold, albeit three times of a tiny percentage – of my having a baby who suffers in some way from some form of physical or intellectual difficulty. And there's an increased chance, particularly if I marry somebody who is epileptic or has it in the family, although my husband doesn't and I don't think it is in his family, of having a child with epilepsy. More realistic difficulties are that the drugs I take will inevitably increase the risk of affecting the foetuses. I haven't asked the consultant about this although I probably should. I'm sure the drugs do have an effect. I remember looking this stuff up in Mimms: all the anti-epilepsy drugs get various bad ratings to various degrees. It was explained to me by a doctor at some point that those drugs that don't have an effect, and only get one bad mark, are rated that way only because nobody has carried out any or many tests on them. It's not safe to assume that they are, therefore, better than the drugs which get many bad marks. So, I believe there is an increased risk and it makes me nervous, and for that reason I would prefer not to have epilepsy.

I'd also like to be able to drive without fear of ever having a fit again. If somebody said I could wave a magic wand and would never have another fit I'd be delighted. But day by day, it doesn't affect my life very much; hardly at all. Having epilepsy may mean that my liver will give out about ten years sooner than it would, but of course I could give up drinking. The drugs do make my body work rather harder to absorb alcohol, and I was told years ago that I shouldn't drink in conjunction with this drug. My last remaining two-finger gesture to the world of epilepsy, and it's not a very sensible adult response, is to continue drinking as and when I will, which is probably doing me horrible damage.

As soon as they know themselves, people with epilepsy should be able to make their own decisions about what they can and cannot do. There may be people who have fits who have absolutely no warning, but I'm sure most people – and I certainly come into this category – have masses of warning. It seems daft to tell people like me to be careful of things like being too close to the road and the like. There are stages when I think I might be going to have a fit, when I think I am probably going to have a fit, and then when I know I'm definitely going to have a fit. So, by the time I'm definitely going to have a fit I will be nowhere near a roadside: I will be lying down somewhere taking my contact lenses out and telling everybody who will listen to me that I am epileptic.

You can't avoid the things in life that might be possibly dangerous. You can't live your life like that. You'd spend your whole life in fear. You have to walk across the road, have a bath, light a gas ring, light candles; you can't live your life avoiding things like that. I think you have to say to yourself, 'There is a possibility I will have a fit and this is how I'll deal with it if I do.' If I am at risk of having a fit, I don't unnecessarily exacerbate the risks. However the rest of life, the 99.999 per cent of my time when I am not going to have a fit, I don't go around thinking about what will happen if I do. I just get on with my life. Otherwise my life would be hideously curtailed, and would be completely dominated by being epileptic which is wholly unnecessary.

People are afraid of epilepsy. If someone is asthmatic and has an attack where they get terribly short of breath (which is absolutely terrifying) you think the person is going to die; and indeed there is that risk I suppose. If someone is diabetic and doesn't have food for too long a period, or doesn't get insulin, then they are in danger of passing out, and once you are unconscious you are presumably in danger of more serious damage: brain damage or ultimately fatality. If those things are not controlled then they are dangerous. Epilepsy is exactly the same, but its physical manifestation is more obviously frightening. I know an asthma attack is absolutely terrifying, but for some reason epilepsy has got a much worse press over the years than the other physical problems.

Epilepsy turns up now and then in literature, associated with madness or genius, and people don't therefore treat it as mundane. They should, because that's what it is. People who have it should see it as mundane; people who come across it should see it as mundane; and that way it wouldn't be a big problem. People don't associate either asthma or diabetes with mental illness of any sort. They're acknowledged as physical things. The thing about epilepsy historically, for some reason, is that it is associated with insanity because it is brain oriented in a way that other physical problems which have physical manifestations are not. And consequently, possibly arising from literature or superstition, people associate epilepsy with the idea of madness or genius. One of the responses I used to get when I was told I was epileptic was a version of 'All the best people are epileptic'. Julius Caesar was epileptic, I think Pope was epileptic, I can't think who else, but it is possible to read off lists of famous and successful and creative people who were epileptic. However, I don't think that's actually the right response. There are millions of people who are epileptic whose lives are not dictated to or not shaped by the fact, and that's how it ought to be.

Otherwise, it leads to situations like people hiding their condition. The only way to deal with that is for everybody who is epileptic to admit it; to deal with it, to tell people. I don't know by name of any other epileptic barrister, but there are at least six or seven of us and statistically therefore there must be others. Somebody did say to me, 'Oh you know so-and-so?

He's epileptic.' I didn't know the name and I've forgotten it, but it's not something which is publicised. In a way, it would be a good thing if everybody who was epileptic was prepared to wear a badge and say, 'I am epileptic'. I think people's ideas about epilepsy would be radically changed because they'd look around and they'd see that all these people, who they'd always thought of as perfectly normal as indeed they are, are in fact epileptic. So that next time somebody mentioned the word epilepsy people wouldn't react negatively, however unconsciously, to the concept.

I haven't considered the idea of the rights of people with epilepsy being allied to the rights of people with other disabilities. I don't actually like the idea of identification on the basis of disability. I can understand drawing strength, in adversity, from the comfort of other people who have undergone the same thing, so this is no criticism of people who do that, but I think that one should treat epilepsy as something to be disregarded as much as that is possible. It is not possible because of the way society responds to epilepsy.

People who come into epilepsy later, as opposed to having it all their lives, often get a dreadful shock, precisely because of the way people think of it, in addition to the limitations like driving, children and so forth. If meeting other people who have epilepsy helps them to feel much better about the fact that they have it too, and insofar as that is a testimony to normalcy, then fine. That, to me, is as far as it should go. But if there's any sense of epileptics getting together to form clubs, then I don't think it's a good thing, because people should think of epilepsy as a minor detail in their life, and not as something by which they identify themselves. I am Suzie Castle, married, a barrister, this that and the next, Suzie to her friends. I'm epileptic, but it's just a peripheral thing. It always has been and always will be no matter how good or bad it is in terms of control.

In a sense, if I was aware of or dealt with anybody who was epileptic I would immediately understand, or have a pretty good idea of, some of the things that they had undergone or experienced. I always feel solidarity with them as a result of other people's reactions. Beyond that, I disapprove of the idea of over-identifying with the idea of epilepsy, because it is the flip-side of the same coin where some people identify those who are epileptic as epileptics first. So for that reason I very much hesitate to identify myself under that label. It's not a matter of being ashamed of epilepsy at all. On the contrary, it's just that I'm not willing to subscribe to a definition of myself that I don't think is relevant.

Barbara Jacobs

Barbara Jacobs is an astrologer, journalist and agony aunt for a number of magazines.

I've been an epileptic all my life, but I didn't discover this until I was older. I was twenty-five, I had a fit at a friend's house and during the fit I'd been incontinent. I was horrified. I was absolutely horrified. I didn't know it was an epileptic fit but because of the experience I went to the doctor. I explained exactly what had happened. He asked whether it had ever happened before and I said 'yes', and explained that this was very similar to other episodes I'd had that my husband had seen. My husband explained what he'd seen and the doctor simply said to me, 'You're epileptic'. It was a terrible thing to throw at somebody of twenty-five. He asked, 'How long have you been experiencing these things?' and I said, 'As long as I can remember.'

I found it very difficult to cope with at first. I knew, of course, that I had been having seizures, that I had had periods of unconsciousness, but I'd been told that they were ordinary fainting attacks.

On top of that my father found it very hard to accept. I think possibly that was because of an incident when I was quite young. I'd been walking up a wooded hill with him, and started to run down. My father had to stop me because I was completely out of control. I just couldn't stop and there were trees in the way. He stopped me by bringing me down in a rugby tackle. Perhaps he felt that had caused the epilepsy, but it hadn't, because I remember I'd had a fit before then. But I think that's what my parents traced it back to: that I'd had a brain injury at that time. So my father always said that I wasn't an epileptic, that it was an exaggeration. I think he found it easier to deny it.

My self esteem was already very badly hurt so I don't think at that time anybody else's opinions would have made it worse or better. As the time went on I found it difficult to accept my father's attitude, but eventually I accepted it as his way of coping. It is one way of coping, just to deny it's there. My Dad comes from a generation that believes that if there's something wrong with your child, it's somehow your fault. I think we can now exonerate ourselves from all blame, this generation and other generations afterwards. If there's anything wrong with my son I don't think 'Oh well, I must have caused it in some way.' I don't think that way. But I think my Dad rather felt guilty and upset, so I can understand the feeling that he had.

It's difficult to say what brings my seizures on. I think stress is the biggest trigger of all but also I get seizures if I have a high temperature or a virus. While being run down might bring my seizures on, I have to say they're actually fantastic in some ways. I suppose I ought to be worried about them and in many ways I am. I try to prevent them coming on. I know they're coming on because I get an aura, and the aura is very peculiar. I get a funny feeling in the top of my nose and sometimes my sense of smell is very much distorted. I get a sound of pins and needles in my head and then I know I'm going to get one, so I go and lie down somewhere convenient and try to talk myself out of it. But that's generally unsuccessful and I go into the fit which I know nothing about, except that I'm going down a very long tunnel and there are people all down this tunnel – people I've known. There's a lot of colour. It's very bright. It's almost a sort of psychedelic feeling going down this tunnel. It's very fast; there's a rushing sound, like the sound of an electric train going through a tunnel. And then, at the end there's a great brightness and I go towards the brightness, all the time feeling really good. It's a marvellous feeling that wants you to go into the brightness, wanting to touch it, and then just as I'm about to go into it, I come out. It's disappointing for the fit to end in a way because the experience of the light is so wonderful and there's such a strong positive feeling. It's as if real life will never be as good as that. It's almost as if all the most marvellous sensory experiences of my life have been distilled into that few minutes when I go down the tunnel.

I always say that I've got built-in electro-convulsive therapy for when I get too big for my boots. Down this comes and I go into a fit and I come out of it being a human being again. I think I've got a very aggressive and assertive personality, and maybe my fits calm me down.

Afterwards, I get a lot of pins and needles in my head and it's real life again and I feel terrible. I feel ill for about forty-eight hours afterwards. Or I feel distracted and very tired. After the forty-eight hours of feeling really bad, a more peaceful me emerges, somebody who's dealt with the stress temporarily.

Despite all that, I'm not in love with the idea of having epilepsy. I would like to be free of fits, especially on the two days afterwards. I suppose there would be something missing if I didn't see what I see when I go into the tunnel. Maybe that's an extra part of me, maybe something that gives me an edge. It's like saying to people how much is your little finger on your left hand part of what you are? Of course, it's a part of you but it isn't something you think about very often. If you'd lost the little finger on your left hand you'd notice it but you don't think about it all that much. I suppose I don't think about my epilepsy very much unless it's threatening. I hate the feeling that I'm going to go into a fit but the experience of having a fit, in itself, is probably part of the urgency that I have in my life.

Nevertheless, if there was a permanent cure I'd take it. It would mean that I could probably live a bit longer. I'm aware that when you have a fit the danger is that you're going to be somewhere that you get yourself into trouble, or perhaps you might kill yourself accidentally during the fit if nobody else was around. For example, I vomited once.

That's something you have to accept. Other people can't really do very much for you when you're having a fit. And in fact, I always say people should do absolutely nothing when I'm having a fit, except to make sure that I don't hurt myself. It's very difficult, because people used to say 'Oh go and put a ruler in their mouth or something, to stop them swallowing their tongue.' People were dying all over the country with lolly sticks being stuck in their mouths and other people were having their fingers bitten off at the first joint. For me, the worst thing is to come round and find somebody cowering away from you.

Most people, although they consider themselves to be broad minded about most things, are quite narrow minded when it comes to fits. It must look, to a lot of people, like demonic possession. I think that's what it comes down to; this is what people's images of epilepsy go back to. Once, I was very heavily pregnant, I was going to an antenatal class and I had to travel by train. As I shut the train door, I shut my hand in it. I was absolutely certain, because of the noise of pins and needles in my head, that I was going to have a fit. So I went into the first compartment along – it was about twenty years ago, when the trains were divided into small compartments – and there was a very pleasant-looking couple sitting there. I said to them, 'Excuse me, I think I'm going to have a fit. Will you make certain that I don't fall off the seat?' I lay on the seat and when I came to, I was lying between the two seats on the floor with the couple cringing in the corner. The man had his arms around the woman as if to protect her from the influence of this satanic being that had just writhed all over the floor. I managed to crawl out of the train and the station master looked after me and gave me a cup of tea, but the couple didn't speak a word. They were silenced by what had happened. I don't know whether to be upset by that or whether to take it as just one of my best humorous memories. It was particularly funny in some ways, blackly funny.

That is the kind of negative reaction you expect, so you don't get too upset about it. What particularly bothers me is getting negative reactions from the kind of people you would think would be enlightenend in some way. That is very upsetting. People who are supposedly educated. People who are in charge of children, for instance: teachers, ministers of religion. Some of these have the most peculiar attitude when you'd think they'd be all right. You learn to judge, though, who to tell about it and who to keep it away from.

Years and years ago, before I became a writer, I was a teacher, and I started to feel ill in the mornings and decided that I wouldn't go into morning assembly. The headmaster discovered, I think from my head of department, that I was avoiding assembly because I was epileptic. I hadn't told the headmaster that I was epileptic. It had only been definitely diagnosed for a few weeks, although, I'd suspected it for many years. It took a long time in those days to actually locate the site of the epilepsy, and so it took a long time for them to say, you *are* epileptic. Anyway, the headmaster called me in, with his deputy, and spent a long time trying to get out of me the fact that I was epileptic, and to admit that was why I wasn't going into assembly. When I finally admitted it, he threatened me with suspension for a fortnight while he examined the whole thing, and maybe permanent suspension. But when the rest of my department threatened to put in their notice if anything was done to me, he withdrew that threat. However, I did notice afterwards that there would be a tame member of staff following me round. The head-master said it was just in case I had a fit at school and I hurt myself. I'd been teaching at the school, by this time, for three years, and had never had a fit at school. I always have fits at night, as I'd explained to the headmaster, but it didn't seem to have gone in.

On the other hand, one of the better experiences in my life was having a baby. The medical staff that I was connected with during my pregnancy didn't bother about the epilepsy at all and they didn't worry me about it. I felt quite good during pregnancy. I only had that one fit and that was at a time when most people might pass out. If anybody else had shut their hand in a door, they would have probably passed out, because it was particularly painful. But I had a fit. So that one fit was quite understandable. I never thought that I'd have a fit during the whole of labour and childbirth. I never even considered it. I never thought, God this pain's getting so bad that I'm going to fit, which is sometimes the case when I have a viral attack. It certainly was the case when I had pneumonia: the pain was so bad I knew I was going to have a fit. But not during childbirth. Remarkably not.

However, there's an epilepsy textbook, apparently (I never looked at it), which says what you're not supposed to do with your new baby. I didn't know anything about it but I was asked to go and address some people in the local health service on the subject of epilepsy. And they were interested to hear my story and how I dealt with the condition. So I told them everything, was very open. I described my seizures, how they happened mostly at night, how they were very infrequent. I thought I painted a picture of someone who wasn't mentally or socially impaired, but someone who occasionally had to lie down or take to bed. Anyway, when I'd finished I took my baby son from my friend who had come along and was holding him for me while I talked. I wandered about chatting to the various people, carrying my son. One of the chief nursing officers came up to me and said, 'I hope you don't carry your baby round when there's nobody there.' I was amazed. This woman should have known better. I'd explained that my epilepsy didn't affect my life in any way. But nevertheless, she was swimming around in the same prejudice as everyone else.

I'd also been warned that you're not supposed to breastfeed. It's supposed to be difficult to get up in the middle of the night and feed your baby, it makes you overtired, and things like that. Well, it's just as well nobody actually spelt it out for me and worried me about it, because none of that happened. I had a very easy pregnancy and it was quite easy child rearing. The fits didn't make any difference at all. The sense of risk wasn't there for me and I never took any special precautions.

Now is that irresponsible, I ask myself? People always accuse epileptics of being irresponsible, as if we are actually going to do things that are bad for us. They are scared of the way we are, so they want us to conform to the way they think is best for us, safe for us. They are making judgements about how we should behave without any understanding of what it is like to be us. We have to judge for ourselves how far what we suffer from is going to be a disability. A doctor said to me, 'You have to sort out how much you can live with and when you can no longer tolerate it, then take a pill. But try to keep everything as easy as possible. Try to keep your life as normal as possible.' I think that's the best way of living with epilepsy. Try not to let it impinge at all, although it will.

I get really angry with the way other people treat me. It can really get to me a lot of the time. I shouldn't let it, but it does. What grates on me is people who think they are being caring: you know, pitying you. What they don't understand is that I don't need their pity. I don't want their pity. It is humiliating and patronising to have some silly person worry about you and feel sorry for you. I'm a person, not some hopeless creature. The stigma has always been there. It still is there. That's why so many people are quiet about their epilepsy. It is why you tell very few people. There are certain jobs where it's easier to talk about it and where there isn't as much stigma. When I really think about it, I wonder if that's got something to do with my being selfemployed. I know that I don't have to rely on other people's opinions of me or other people's judgements of me. I don't have to tell them I'm an epileptic. I don't have to discuss it at all if I don't wish to. And, in my job, people tend to be far more broad minded than in other jobs or other areas I've operated in.

However, it doesn't stop the stigma just because the people around me are more pleasant about it. It doesn't stop it being a stigma. It's an appalling stigma. There is always a feeling that it's associated with witchcraft. It is associated with being possessed. And you sense also that other people imagine that if you're an epileptic, you must be mentally handicapped. You must be mentally damaged in a way that's going to affect your reason as well. That attitude has come from doctors as much as from history. We find ourselves pushed into a very defensive position of saying 'Listen, I've got epilepsy but I'm very, very bright.' And so it throws you back all the time on that sort of defensiveness. You feel you have to boast about academic achievements or about your intelligence because people are continually questioning. You can see their eyes, you can see their face change when you say you're epileptic. They start to look at you as they might at an animal howling. Isn't that awful, to be an animal or something? Nice enough to have around, but not in their home. It makes me absolutely furious. I hate it. I hate other people's attitude. I hate living with epilepsy because of that. The experience of a seizure itself is not all that bad.

Why don't people feel this way about other chronic illnesses? Why do they feel so strongly toward epilepsy? It makes me touchy about anything that could be an insult that might possibly be connected with my epilepsy: for example, if people say something about me being witchy or anything. Whereas most people would take it just as a sort of joke, with me it goes a lot deeper. Somebody once said they were going to put me on the bonfire on bonfire night, because I was a witch. It was only a rather nasty childish joke, but immediately my mind connected with what they used to do to witches. They weren't really witches, they were ordinary people suffering with epilepsy. Ordinary women with epilepsy.

It's very hard to know what could be done to change society's attitude towards us, what could be done to make people think of you as just having another chronic illness like asthma. It would be lovely to be thought of as an asthmatic or a diabetic. One of the things that could be done is to change the name: epilepsy has a particularly nasty connotation. When I was a child the word 'spastic' was widely used as an insult, and it was changed to cerebral palsy. It might be a good idea if a nice long word like 'neuro-paroxysm' was used to try to confuse people, and also to try to convince people that this is just another medical condition.

We have not been touched by the devil. We haven't been made into less than human beings. But at the same time I don't want to be at the forefront of some kind of political movement, campaigning for epileptics. I hope that we can do it on a one-to-one basis. I think that's the way it's getting done.

Ironically, though, in order to earn money for people who are seriously damaged, not by epilepsy, but have serious mental problems of which epilepsy is merely a symptom, then it's necessary to build up the 'victim' image of epilepsy. We're victims, really, of social attitude and that implies – conveys – a kind of powerlessness. And strangely, I do feel powerless about epilepsy generally. This is unusual because I don't generally feel powerless about anything, but my epilepsy is somehow a very personal issue.

I hope that I'd be able to persuade other people that it isn't the horrific social problem that they consider it to be, but I don't think I would want to be part of a politicising movement. Epileptics of the world unite, we have nothing to lose but our covens! There are so many different kinds of epilepsy. There are so many different kinds of problems that we all have to face, and in a way we're getting to a point where epilepsy isn't my problem, it's theirs. Out there: they have the problem with epilepsy. I don't have a problem with my own epilepsy, except in trying to deal with other people's attitudes towards me.

There has been an occasional change in my friends' attitudes, for example. Some of them are now a lot gentler with me, which is awful. It's the sign of pity, of care. In other words, 'This isn't the same feisty woman we used to know. This is somebody with a problem'. At first, somebody takes you for what you are. They accept you as stroppy, bad tempered, difficult; you have an awful sense of humour, are a very wounding sort of person; big headed, assertive and noisy. Then you say to them, 'By the way, I'm an epileptic,' and suddenly, a little cloud comes over their eyes and you can see them thinking, 'Oh, it's that old thing: the epileptic person. Now of course these people feel persecuted. And we all know that epileptics are manic depressives, so we can excuse her behaviour. So when she's just ranting and raving about something or other that we don't think matters, we can say "Oh well, she's not concerned, she's not a crusader, she's not a campaigner, she's not just being generally stroppy: she's a poor old epileptic."'

In the end, you've got to laugh. When I was first put on the epilepsy medication it had a terrible effect on me – awful – because they put you on phenobarbitone at first. There's a funny story associated with this. I live in an area where there are a lot of alcoholics, and one of the alcoholics came up to me just before Christmas and said, 'Have you got – Can you spare me some money? I'm a poor old alcoholic, I need a drink, and I'm also an epileptic.' So I said to him, 'Oh I'm an epileptic too.' And he said, 'Are you? Got any pills?'

Paul Savill

Paul Savill left school six years ago. He worked for a year before being made redundant. He has been unemployed since then. His epilepsy was diagnosed nine years ago.

I'm not sure what brings on my seizures. Occasionally it can be flashing lights, like strobes. But most of the time I can't really tell. It just seems to be no reason at all. I don't see or hear anything when I have a seizure. Before I have a seizure, I sometimes get a strange feeling in my stomach, as a warning. But, apart from that, I just see blackness and then wake up with a big headache. I just pass out. I don't know what I'm doing in between. Afterwards I feel, as they say, 'Sick as a parrot, Brian!' I just have a bad, bad headache, full stop, and just want to sleep.

My seizures vary. Sometimes I go a bit semi-conscious and I start rubbing my arm, or doing repetitive things. My arm might jerk a little and then I come out of it and I feel confused for a short while (myclonic jerks). My other type of seizure is the classic one – a tonic-clonic – that's when I fall down and throw my arms and legs about, uncontrollably. I have no voluntary movement over my body; everything I do is involuntary. And then after a while, I come round.

People shouldn't try to stop me or hold me down. I should be left alone, basically, but if I am in danger or in danger of hurting people, they could try to move me out of the way or maybe stick something under my head, and that's about it until I come round. But of course what people actually do when I'm having a seizure is very different to that. Some people run around panicking. Many people have stuck their fingers in my mouth and almost lost them. Most of the time I've let people know what to do when I've met them. It's just when I'm walking along the street when nobody knows me that I encounter people who don't know what to do.

Funnily enough, a few odd things have happened to me when I've been having a seizure. I was accused of rape once, when I had a seizure and fell on top of somebody and just threw my arms and legs about, but luckily I know several police officers, who I go camping and hiking with, who helped me out of that particular sticky situation. I've also gone abseiling and canoeing and had a seizure in that sort of situation.

People might be amazed by the fact I do those sorts of things, but they shouldn't be. Everything I do has several precautions but having epilepsy doesn't stop me from doing anything anybody else would do. If I have a fit while abseiling, I have a safety rope. The others just let me down, wind me down gently while I'm having a fit and then, when I come round and feel I can carry on, I carry on. When I'm canoeing there's more than one more person keeping an eye on me, so two people can help me out if I ever capsize and have a fit. Rock climbing is basically the same as abseiling, although I can't do pot-holing. The main fact is having enough people to rely on. If I have a fit, it can be deadly, and they understand about that. I've had one fit while abseiling and all they did was just leave me up there while I was throwing my arms and legs about and then lower me down when I stopped so I didn't hit anybody. I've been canoeing and had a seizure. Two people automatically came to my aid, rectified my boat and then just let me throw my arms around, throw myself about for a while. They kept the boat upright so I didn't drown, and dragged me into the side.

If people react by saying I'm taking far too many risks, I would say it's my choice. I am willing to take these risks. I would understand if they objected because it's dangerous to other people. While I would stop in that instance, generally I am willing to take the risks, otherwise I'm not going to lead a normal life. The epilepsy would take control of my life and I want to take control of my epilepsy. I'm not trying to be superman. I'm just trying to show that epilepsy does not mean you're bedridden or you stay at home all the time. You can lead a normal life. You can do all the things that everybody else can do, with a few exceptions. I do heed the guidelines that are generally given out for people with epilepsy, about taking baths, and the like. I always have somebody in the house while I have a bath and leave the door unlocked so if I do have a fit they have easy access to help me. Most of the time I have a shower anyway. For everything I do there are safety precautions. I'm not doing anything that can endanger me, and other precautions are covered by friends and people.

My parents don't mind the lifestyle I lead, as long as I lead it with caution. Everything I do is in moderation. I try not to overdo it. My mother tried to molly-coddle me and my dad decided that I wouldn't get anywhere if I stayed wrapped up, never doing anything and always relying on my mother. In the end, my mum gave in and let me live my own life. Now, I don't rely on as many people as I used to. I rely on my doctor and a few other people. I always rely on other people when I do adventurous things, including having a bath, and I think that's about it really. My parents don't necessarily mind.

When I first discovered that I had epilepsy, I looked it up in a dictionary and I was confused because I didn't know what to do. I didn't know how badly it was going to affect my life. I just didn't know, so, once I started having quite a few fits, I was determined not to let it beat me, not to let it get me down. Because of that, I think, I've led a more adventurous life than I would normally have had.

School wasn't easy after that, I suppose. There were some incidents. I was bullied; well, they tried to bully me but had to give up because in the end I knew more jokes about epilepsy than they did. There were also some bullies that always wanted to hit you. One decided to hit me on the back of my head and at that time, that would cause a fit. So, when he hit me on the back of the head, I had a fit and threw my arms out and knocked him to the ground. I came round and got up before he stood up, and he never gave me trouble after that. Unfortunately, that has happened to friends as well. I've been with friends at times when I didn't feel well. So I told them that I was going to lie down and have a rest; maybe have a fit. There was a couple of people keeping an eye on me, but one of my best friends came running up saying, 'Out of the way, out of the way, I know what I'm doing. Paul's having a fit. I know what to do.' He bent down and said, 'Are you okay?' My fist went up and knocked him back, four feet off the ground, and again, I got up before he did.

At school, there were teachers who were scared of me or worried about what would happen if I had a fit. They wouldn't show it, but they wouldn't have me in their class either. They wouldn't let me know that was the reason. They wouldn't say 'I'm not having you in my class because you have epilepsy'. They would turn round and say 'You have the wrong attitude for this class' or things like that. They'd try and cover it up. So I was put down, or sent along to different teachers who didn't mind.

At the time, the school that I went to had a problem believing what I said about how I was feeling. They over-reacted to the fit. If I had a fit in class and came round, I would tell them I was okay to go back to the lesson, but they wouldn't have it. They wouldn't take my word for it. They would send me straight home. At that time I was having about a fit a day. So I was being sent home, missing lessons that I could have been doing quite easily, every day, or every other day. I knew I would be passed out for, at the most, half an hour each day, and then be able to go back to the class. But with all this sending home I achieved very low grades.

I did exams. They put me in a room, on my own, in case I had a fit. Nobody to keep an eye on me: they just locked me in a room, let me do my exam, let me out when I finished and that was it. But I lost out on a grade because I started doing the exam, opened the page, had a fit, and because nobody came in, nobody was there to see me have this fit. So, when I came round, they took me out and sent me home, and they wouldn't let me take the exam again because I'd already seen the paper. It was pointless and I couldn't take the previous year's exam because that was the first year of GCSEs rather than GCEs and CSEs, so I got an ungraded for it. I think I was cheated really over that. I had a fit in the Art exam and tried to get away with saying it was modern art, but they wouldn't have it, because I threw paints all over the place. That was a joke on them, of course, but I would say I was treated as a second-class citizen at school, to a certain extent.

After I finished at school, I went to work. I started at an accountants, and had fits now and again. Again, they wouldn't believe what I would say about how I felt, and so they sent me home. That happened about once a week, maybe twice, and so they more or less said 'Any more fits, and you're out'. The next fit came along, and a few weeks later I was given the sack for not being able to keep up with the work-load, despite the fact that I was doing other clerical work, after I'd done my set load. That was beyond the point as far as they were concerned. They sacked me because I couldn't keep up with the work-load according to them. But I could. I felt cheated but I realised it was a business, that they had to make a profit and they had been losing some money, but I still felt cheated.

Everybody sees epilepsy as my problem. Epilepsy is not my problem. It's something I suffer from. I don't worry about it all the time. Epilepsy seems to be other people's problem: in how to deal with it; that they do not believe what I say about how I feel. They panic and they think I'm possessed by the devil or something. As well, I have had people not willing to be friends with me because I have epilepsy. I have even had friends being stupid about it. Once, for a laugh, I sneezed towards a friend, and just for a joke I said 'You've caught epilepsy'. He was running around in a panic for thirty seconds and then all of a sudden he went 'Hang on, you can't catch epilepsy like that'. Just the reaction was awful. It's crazy to think that you could suggest that someone could catch epilepsy from something like that, and for them to be ignorant enough to believe it.

At school they did call me 'Epi!' I wasn't exactly called other names, but people tried to hurt me by telling jokes that might upset me. Unfortunately that sort of thing doesn't. I know more epileptic jokes than most people. I went round school with the name Epi, but it didn't bother me. People who knew me called me by my name. Other people were trying to be hurtful and I just wouldn't let them. When I told better epilepsy jokes, several people would turn round to me and say 'You can't say that. Cor, that's not the sort of thing you can say', or 'You've got epilepsy, you can't tell those jokes'. I told them, 'Who's got more right to tell the jokes, me or you?'.

I've had several girlfriends. Epilepsy hasn't affected that much, not really. Enough said.

Some of my drugs make me feel drowsy, but, apart from that, they're not a problem. I've always taken drugs since I started having my fits; I've never stopped taking them. I've relied on the doctors. For all I know, I could have no effects afterwards if I didn't take the drugs but I don't believe that is true. My doctor, not my GP, but my main doctor, I trust him completely. He knows what he's talking about. He believes what I tell him, how I feel and he reacts according to how I feel and what I tell him. And he's a really nice guy.

Going back to college was a lot different to school because they treated me like an adult. They reacted to how I told them I felt. If I said I could go back to work they'd let me go back to work and because of that I got better grades. I also made a lot more friends. The tutors haven't reacted to me in any way, but treated me like every other student, so, it's the way I've always wanted it to be at school but it never was. With better grades, my job prospects are still not great but they're better. I keep applying for jobs. I keep trying, but due to the climate we're in at the moment, I just don't seem to get any jobs offered. There are lots of other people who are probably better qualified for the job and, of course, there's still employers that feel, or are, ignorant about epilepsy and so they feel they can't take me on.

Many of my mates at college, have got jobs. When I apply for jobs, every single application form has a health question on it about epilepsy, blackouts, or fits. I always answer truthfully. I feel it's in my best interests. So I'm not hiding anything: I'm showing them who I am, exactly what I've got, so they know what they're dealing with when I walk in the door for the interview. But I don't get many interviews. Maybe I should hide it, but I just feel I should let them know. Otherwise, if I hide it, everybody else is going to start hiding how they feel about the epilepsy and how they react. If I hide how I feel about epilepsy how is everybody else going to start feeling: 'Oh I'd better not show what I am like.' The employers might feel that the person's not responsible enough with his epilepsy to take on this position because he didn't tell them straight off. You know, if you lie they might hold it against you.

How am I supposed to get anywhere? I've filled in numerous application forms – nearly a hundred – and in that time I've had less than ten interviews. At the interviews I've had they did discuss the epilepsy issue. Some people – well, two of them – just said 'Do you have epilepsy?' and I said 'Yes' and they went 'Fine'. The others asked me about what drugs I take, how often I have my fits and I answered them. They didn't exactly seem worried about it, although they may have been. If they were worried about it, to a great extent, they wouldn't have given me an interview, but they didn't give me the job, either. They didn't give me a job, although there may have been other applicants who were better qualified.

I feel unhappy about not having a job but I don't feel very depressed. I'm still determined to get a job, to keep going. It just makes me more determined to carry on and show that I can lead a normal life. Quite a few of my friends have got jobs and there are others without jobs as well.

About equal numbers of my friends do and don't have jobs, so I don't feel that left out. I do voluntary work at the college I was at, just to keep myself motivated. Just to stay in the 9 to 5 system. I'm very good with computers, so that's the kind of work I am trying for. I do some temping in that field, but I think a lot of companies, when I apply for a job, think I can't do it because of the VDU screens and suchlike. I write to explain that only a very small percentage of people with epilepsy have photo-sensitive epilepsy, and that I'm okay in that sense, but they never write back.

So I try to keep busy. I do some canoeing or whatever, and I'm taking up surfing now. My epilepsy is improving slightly these days. When it all gets me down I just go and have a good time with my friends. When I'm with them, well I'm one of them. I'm not normal, but I'm one of the lads. It's only when I pass out that they treat me any differently.

Frances Hassler

Frances Hassler is Director of GLAD, the Greater London Association of Disabled people.

My epilepsy started when I was thirteen, so that makes it more than twenty-five years that I've had the condition. I was diagnosed when I was fifteen, and at the time I really wasn't personally all that distressed. I don't think that I knew what the ramifications would be later, in terms of career moves and things like that. At that time it was a nuisance, but it wasn't deeply emotionally distressing. The worst thing was having to take the drugs which were absolutely horrible. I hated that part of the condition. Most anti-epileptic drugs have side effects, and the first thing I was put on was phenobarbitone (anti-convulsant drug, now rarely prescribed). The only way I can describe the effects to people who have never taken it, is that it's like living with a very thick plate of glass between you and the rest of the world. You could see people talking and know there's some message that is supposed to be coming through and that it's not quite reaching. It's a really horrible feeling. The other drugs I was on subsequently were not so bad, although one made me desperately ill. Well, it poisoned me, but suffice to say that they're just not good things to be taking long term.

In one sense, I'm not too keen to be talking to a wide audience about the physical nature of my epilepsy. I think it's a message that gets misused,

31

although people do have to know about it so that epilepsy isn't talked about in whispers. But there are many books and videos about the physical side of epilepsy: what happens and what to do. I prefer to talk about epilepsy in terms of how people react to me, that is, the social aspects of the condition. Broadly speaking, very standard things tend to bring on my seizures: lack of sleep, too much alcohol, stress, arguments, those sorts of things. When I do have a seizure I see and feel very little. I get very little warning, I'm out cold, and I have absolutely no consciousness at all when it's going on. Afterwards I am disoriented, tired and sleepy. That's how it is for me.

For others it's very different. I've talked to other people with epilepsy about their experiences. Some of them chime in with mine and I think 'Oh yes that feels like me', and other people have something completely different. The trouble is there are lots of different sorts of epilepsy. It's a very 'catch-all' term for all sorts of different things that happen to you.

Physically we are all different, but in terms of how people react to us there is a great deal of overlap. When someone is having a seizure, the best thing is to leave them alone, unless they're in real physical danger of rolling into the fire, or something. Just leave them be because there's absolutely nothing you can do, and you're not going to help them by grabbing hold of them or anything like that. There's a lot of talk about whether one should call an ambulance or not: you know, to be safe rather than sorry. For me, that highlights one of the problems with the condition: that people don't know about it. It doesn't get talked about. Somehow, for all sorts of reasons, people have a history of hiding it away so others aren't certain. If you know it's an epileptic fit, you probably don't need to call an ambulance. If you don't know what it is and you think someone might need to go to hospital, common sense says call the ambulance. Let somebody else who does know about it deal with it.

Getting away from the physical effects, the effects on my life, as such, started at school. Initially, I guess I missed quite a lot of school when I was doing my O levels. After that, I caught up, so that it probably affected slightly how I did in the short term, not in the long term. My parents, I think, were quite distressed at first. It's a bit of a shock when your child gets something potentially quite serious like that, but they were very good about it. My mother used to come to the hospital with me on a regular basis until I felt happy going on my own and they adjusted to it fairly well. I guess they were quite protective in the early years. They didn't want me to do too much in case it provoked more fits, but on the whole they were just quite ordinary about it really.

When I went to university I didn't tell most people about it, initially. I didn't think it really mattered whether they knew or not. At university, everything's new, everything's different, and the thing that made me different is that I used to shake a lot in the mornings and drop things – and drop my breakfast. To me, that was just everyday normality because that's what I did. One or two fellow students would think it was a bit odd and I'd explain why, but on the whole it wasn't a major big deal. I didn't avoid doing things because of having epilepsy. I still stayed up all night and drank too much and did all the other things that students do. I did all of that. So I don't think it made much difference at all. I certainly didn't pay much attention to any of the guidelines for safe behaviour handed out by the various associations and charities. There's a lot of stuff that's written about epilepsy that seems to apply to somebody else, who's not me, who's got the condition. I don't feel that they concern me. The epileptic person they're talking about just doesn't seem to be me.

All that stuff I've seen is very negative. It's all very well saying epilepsy needn't ruin your life as if somehow we all expect epilepsy *will* ruin our lives. I've never thought it was going to, and so all this stuff just comes across to me as incredibly negative. It seems just that the whole message is that you've got to be afraid of this, afraid of that, afraid of the other. That didn't feel like my experience and so I never took any notice at all of that. Some people, probably people who don't have epilepsy might say I was being irresponsible, but it's none of their business. It's up to me to decide what risks I take in life, just as it's up to them to decide what risks they take in life. People seem to be focussed in on what is going to happen if you have a fit, but I think that it's not the worst thing in the world to have a fit. Sure, having a fit in a public place is a thing at the back of your mind as a worry. But it's very much at the back; it's not there as a daily anxiety. You have to live.

I didn't have any particular difficulties forming relationships at university. There was no big problem in having to announce 'I have epilepsy'. It wasn't like that. I think any difficulties that there might have been were not about epilepsy at all. By the time you know someone well enough that you feel you need to tell them that you have epilepsy, you know them well enough anyway. You've already made the relationship and it's there. Very occasionally I was disappointed at a friend's reaction when I told them I had epilepsy. Sometimes you get those who take a step back as if it's contageous. That's both annoying and upsetting, but then you just think 'Well, that's their problem'. Mostly what has happened is people have displayed a morbid curiosity about the usual, 'Should I stick a spoon in your mouth when you have a fit?' and things like that. It gets tedious, but it's not disappointing. It's just boring.

Another reaction that I found disappointing was that of the medical profession. Generally, I have found doctors not to be very good on epilepsy. I was technically still a child when I was diagnosed and so they spoke to my mother, not to me. They didn't tell me anything, and I wasn't given any useful information about my condition. I was told a whole string of things I shouldn't do, but actually no useful information about it at all. So, my experience with doctors hasn't been happy. I don't think this is unique to epilepsy. I think it's probably the case for anybody with a disability or a serious health condition: doctors don't really communicate very well with their patients. I think that that's true for all sorts of conditions. For things where they haven't actually got a cure they can offer you, they're even worse at communicating with you, because they like to make people better. I think people probably go into medicine because they would like to make people better but, of course, they can't if you've got a condition which essentially has no cure. Someone should ask doctors why they are like that.

If doctors came along with some sort of cure I'm not sure I'd take it. I'm quite happy living the way I am, really. That might sound strange, but you get used to the whole way your body is. There are all sorts of things about my body that maybe if I'd been designing it from the ground up, I'd have done differently. However, it's the one I've got and it's the one that I live with, and I'm quite happy with it. If I had another body tomorrow, a body free of epilepsy, I think I would feel jolly strange. You'd have to get to used to a whole range of differences. It would be pretty odd.

After I left university I faced the big wide world of work. Finding jobs was really the first time when I realised that people with epilepsy were discriminated against, because as soon as I went to apply for jobs it became an issue. I was working in the health service, and at that stage, and I think still now, you have to fill in a form about your health when you apply. I wasn't allowed to start in my first job until they had a letter from my consultant saying that I was able to work. It actually meant quite a long delay in taking up the post and I had to go and sign on while I was waiting for that. It was wholly unnecessary and a bit ironic because it was a big psychiatric hospital where people were having fits left, right and centre every day. It seemed to me an extraordinary thing that they had to wait to let me come to work in that setting until my consultant had said 'it's all right, she can do it.'

I have to say I think the NHS deals very bureaucratically and nervously with all sorts of disabled employees. I don't think this is unique to epilepsy. I think that other people with disabilities who have become employed or tried to become employed in the NHS have found that it's not a very user-friendly employer in that sense. Partly it's because the NHS is used to thinking of disabled people as its product, as patients and not as colleagues. The difficulty is in making that adjustment somehow. You would think that they should be good at dealing with disability because it's there every day, but they're only good if you're playing your correct role, and that's the patient one. Once you step outside of that, people have difficulties with it.

Eventually I decided to leave the Health Service for a number of reasons. One of these was connected with my epilepsy. I had a fit while I was working and it caused a bit of a fuss. It seemed to me at the time that it was going to stay being something which would provoke a negative response from my employers. Ultimately it seemed it would have an effect on my career prospects. You'd get those people who would always be asking – usually with the best intentions but sometimes not – whether I could deal with this or that sort of stress. At that time, and this is going back some years, it was difficult enough already being a woman and trying to make a career in management. So on top of that, being an epileptic woman trying to make a career in management, it just seemed to me like an unnecessarily difficult effort. I also decided I wanted to work in something a bit more directly involving people: something more to do with welfare or counselling or social work. Something like that. So there were a number of reasons why I moved, but the management's reaction to my epilepsy was one of them.

I went to work for the Spinal Injuries Association which is a national self-help group for paralysed people, and set up their welfare service. I don't feel I was opting out going to work with other disabled people, partly because the job at the Spinal Injuries Association was at least as difficult as anything one could do in mainstream work. It was at least as challenging, and I did that because I could do something creative, useful and important. It doesn't feel like a cop-out. I think it has been easier for me to make a career in the disability movement, because something that was a handicap outside has a distinct advantage in the movement. I know that I've been able to take that advantage and because I have experience of epilepsy, I can talk about disability and work with other disabled people from a position of knowledge, from a position of comradeship. I don't know if that's quite the right word, but somehow you fit. We're all in the same movement together. I don't think that's a cop-out.

This issue of disability is an emotive area, and the issue of 'Is epilepsy a disability?' is a wide one. I think there are some pretty obvious answers to that. When you're saying that we've all got a disability and that epilepsy is part of the disability movement, it's crass and facile to say that it is the same as being blind or being in a wheelchair. Quite clearly, if I'm out with my friend in a wheelchair, her problem is that she can't get on the bus. My problem is I'm not allowed to drive the bus. Two rather different sorts of experience, and the day-to-day frustration of the person in the wheelchair is much greater than mine in that respect. Not being able to travel about is much more annoying than not being able to follow a certain career path, so obviously it's different. On the other hand, and having said that, I know people with epilepsy who don't use the bus either, and that's because they have fits unpredictably and quite often they're not certain that they are not going to end up under the bus instead of on the bus. So some of the issues are very similar even though functionally they might be different. Disabled people have difficulty using public transport for a whole range of reasons.

At the same time there isn't a league table or pecking order of disabilities and we shouldn't be trying to fit epilepsy into one. It would be easier to talk about bringing people with epilepsy into the disability movement, because I think there's actually two processes we have to go through to come into the disability movement as a person with epilepsy. First of all you have to say 'yes, I am a disabled person', and that can be difficult. If you have a condition that is easy to conceal, by defining yourself disabled you decide to join a group of people who actually are devalued in society. You have to make a personal decision to come out from behind the camouflage and sit up or stand up and be counted. Then you have the second stage which is 'am I a good enough or a real disabled person?' Being a little inconvenienced isn't the same as using a wheel-chair, for example. So then there's that self doubt about 'am I? Do I really deserve to be here?'

When you get in a position like mine you also have to think 'am I being used because I am an easy disabled person to cope with?' I don't have a speech impairment. People don't have to bother to put things in Braille for me. It's very easy for non-disabled people, who want to find a spokes-person for disability, to deal with someone who is really easy to cope with, to come to someone like me and not have to engage with the general reality of disability.

People with epilepsy do share much with all other disabled people. It's just that there isn't a strong voice for epilepsy within the movement, and many people with epilepsy don't want to be anything to do with that idea. I think it is partly because we are concealed from one another. If you start talking to people about having epilepsy, you'll suddenly find a whole chain of people who've got it too, but, of course, you can't just walk into a crowd and say 'oh, they're the ones who are epileptic'. We're concealed from each other. That is partly due to the history of shame about the con-dition. Also, maybe the things that we are striving for in civil rights terms are not as easily characterized as in some other areas of disability. I'm not absolutely certain.

It seems to me that there is quite a lot to strive for. In some ways, the things that we want – for example, a lack of discrimination at work – are general to all disabled people. It seems better to get into the main strug-gle and say that anti-discrimination legislation is good for us all, rather than say that 'Because I'm epileptic I want it'. It's much more important to say 'Because I'm epileptic, because this person is blind and that person is paralysed, we all want anti-discrimination legislation'. There isn't the same motivation, I guess, for us to get into a separate political struggle, but there is a very strong motivation for us to be in that broad political struggle.

I recognize that many people with epilepsy are desperate to be thought of as normal and not as disabled. I think I might have thought that myself once, because my view of disability was people in wheelchairs, people with white canes, people who were very sick, and if that was what dis-ability was then that certainly wasn't me. But now I think that what we share with all disabled people is our experience of discrimination. We also share other things like the disempowering effect of going through the medical system. But the thing that we share most essentially is our experience of discrimination and that I think is what makes epilepsy like other disabilities in a way. Also, some people with epilepsy are quite physically limited in what they can do, mostly as a result of side effects of having had fits or having taken drugs for a long time. Therefore to say that epilepsy is just the momentary thing that happens when you have the fit that affects your brain is a bit over-simple. There's more happening in people's lives than that.

It isn't the medical condition that makes the disability. It's actually the social result of that, and the discrimination in particular, that makes the disability. That's why I feel allied to the disabled persons' movement and part of it: through that shared experience. I don't pretend that my experience is the same as other disabled people; there's a whole range of difference in what happens. It's also different if you've grown up with a disability than if you acquire a disability in adult life. The only thing that we can say is the same for all of us, is the experience of discrimination.

As soon as I went to work in the the disability movement, a lot of things started to make sense to me. There was a whole different way of looking at my experience and I met people that I could relate to: people who could talk about their conditions or their impairments in ways that began to make a lot of sense to me. It's very fulfilling working in the disability movement at the moment because it's alive, it's very vibrant. There's a lot of work going on that seems to be going somewhere. Not only is it a very comfortable place to work as a person with epilepsy, it's also really interesting, and I work with a lot of extremely interesting, pleasant and exciting people. So, in all those sorts of ways it's a job that really suits me.

Some of my friends and family can't quite understand why I want to do this. They think it's a bit odd to want to work with all these disabled people, because even friends and family still see disabled people as 'those others', as sad, as unfortunate. They can't quite understand why I actually want to be part of that group. Other members of my family and other friends actually understand what I'm on about when I say that this feels powerful to me. Disabled people don't feel pathetic, sad and tragic to me and, after all, they make up a large block of my friends and peer group. Some family members understand that, and some friends understand that more than others.

What I would say to the person with epilepsy who says 'That this is all very well but I am normal and I want to have nothing to do with the notion of being disabled' is two things. One is, of course, in a common-sense way epilepsy is normal. Lots and lots of people have epilepsy; that's very normal. But people who are trying to distance themselves from disabled people by saying 'I'm not one of them', have made the mistake of internalizing all the negative stuff about disability. In a sense, they are almost trying to shut off a part of their lives and say 'the bit you see when I'm standing up looking normal is the reality, and the bit you see when I'm down on the floor rolling around is not really me.' And since it can't be particularly psychically healthy to try and split yourself in two, it also seems to me it's very isolating to say that. To say 'I'm going to get on with this little condition all by myself, and not relate to the other disabled people in society, because they are a devalued bunch of people I don't want to be part of'. Because then, there's no possibility of progress. You are on your own with the condition, and it's only by identifying other people who've got, not the same experience as you, but the same category of experience as you, that you are ever going to make any progress forward.

The other side to this is that the movement to get civil rights for disabled people needs people with epilepsy. We are still some way off getting anti-discrimination legislation for disability. In the House of Commons there is very broad support for it on one side and there's a tiny trickle of support on the other side. Given political reality, until we can make that trickle of support on the Government side into a swell, we're not going to get anywhere. It's very important that we carry on pushing the case for it, because today, an employer can dismiss me because I'm epileptic; no other reason has to be given. If I'm an employer and I'm determined not to employ you because you have epilepsy then there's really nothing that people can do to prevent that happening. On the other hand, let's say there is anti-discrimination legislation tomorrow. If I can prove that the reason that you haven't given me the job is because of the epilepsy, then at least I have some comeback. No one pretends that the sex-discrimination laws and the race-discrimination laws are perfect. Discrimination still happens widely. But it gives you some sort of a peg to start chipping away and to say 'I've got a right to be there'. At the moment we don't have a right. It's quite legal to discriminate against us, and we can't really go back to people and say 'The law says you can't do this to me'. The law says actually you can. And if the law was there, at the very least you could say 'You can't do this!' You still may end up without a job, but to me it feels more powerful to have the law on your side.

While it seems unlikely that people with epilepsy would lose their jobs because of it in this day and age, it really does still happen. Ignorance is rife. I've certainly come across a number of people working in education who, when their fits have been discovered, or they've started to have fits, have lost their jobs on the rather odd grounds that they can't keep charge of a class of children if they have a fit. That, and that they have been dismissed from their jobs seems to me patent nonsense.

There's several other people who have been in contact with GLAD who have not been offered jobs they're well qualified for. The employers found out that they had epilepsy, even though there was nothing in the job that would be put at risk: these are desk jobs. There's nothing about climbing up scaffolding or anything that might be remotely dangerous in it. I tend to think in all employment discrimination, employers have this rather odd idea in their heads that people are irrational, that they apply for jobs they can't do. My experience is that most people apply for jobs they can do and that disabled people are no different to anybody else. We wouldn't automatically put ourselves at risk in a job. There is a lot of very unthinking knee-jerk discrimination in employment. And that makes me feel angry and frustrated. Sometimes I want to get up and seize people by the throat and shake them and say 'don't be so stupid!' People are not going to apply for this job if they don't feel it's well within their capabilities.

I'm not sure if it would be worth people with epilepsy deciding to register as disabled. I went through this question, about whether I should register for employment purposes. One part of me says 'yes', you should register, because the registers should be complete and everybody should know how many disabled people there are in the workforce. Therefore we should all do it. The other part of me says that if you go for a job and tick the box to say I'm a registered disabled person, your chances of getting that job have just gone down by maybe three to one. It is a difficult decision for each person to make, but there's very little benefit for a person with epilepsy. The only tangible benefits I've ever found is that if you need particular equipment to do the job, you can get it through the employment service. It is a tangible benefit if that's what you need, but if not I haven't found a single tangible benefit of registration. I don't think that the registration method, whether it's for Social Services or for employment, is a useful tool. It's a Government tool, and not actually useful to people with epilepsy.

Above all, it would be useful for people with epilepsy to change society's view, to improve their situation in society. One of the most important things that we can do is be open about our condition and not to go along with the conspiracy of silence and shut ourselves away. It does mean being a little bit patient when people ask you all the usual routine questions, in order to try and take away the mystery around the condition. There's nothing mysterious, nothing strange. Some people have fits is all it is.

I've never hidden my epilepsy. Since I've been working with the disability movement, working for GLAD, or before that working for the Spinal Injuries Association, I don't think that I ever needed to. It's not a question of concealing anything. Before that, when I was at university and working in the Health Service, I would play it down. I have epilepsy but it doesn't really affect me, it doesn't really make a difference to my life. That's just colluding with the whole denial process, but on the other hand I have to be honest and say, actually it doesn't make a lot of difference to my life. It's not a major disaster for me at all. It would be wrong and misleading to say that it was.

I think it's helpful if people do 'come out', but if someone has a private reason for concealing it, because of fear of losing their job or something, I don't think I can beat them over the head and say you've got to come out and be part of the movement. I think that's asking too much.

I do recognize that it is hard to be 'out'; at ease with one's own epilepsy. Society is very focused on the medical aspects of our epilepsy, on what it's safe and unsafe for us to do, but we are the ones who are left with the effects of society's decisions and attitudes about us. What happens to you when you have epilepsy is that various people decide various things in your life: the law decides that you can't drive, and it decides that even if you haven't had a fit for a very long time, you can't drive large things like buses and trucks. It can also be decided for you that you would be better off in a special school, in a sheltered environment rather than in a mainstream school, that somehow you're too delicate to be in an ordinary school. Other people can decide for you that you really need to live somewhere special, that because you maybe have fits fairly often, that you can't cope in an ordinary house, in an ordinary environment. So they set up little colonies for people with epilepsy. The result of all that stuff is that people are segregated and moved away from the mainstream of society and that's all extremely disempowering. That's the extreme of the social effect of epilepsy. The other side of it is that it can be inconvenient and painful. Having fits in public places is another social side, on a more personal level.

Society makes you feel, very strongly, that epilepsy is your problem and it's nothing to do with society. That's the case for all people with a disability. I don't think it's unique to epilepsy. Most people see it as an individualized problem: that epilepsy happens to *you*. You have to cope with it and accept that you're really asking rather a lot for people to accommodate to our physical realities. We're all supposed to accommodate to the mythical physical reality of a very fit, young, probably male person that most of us are not.

There's also a hell of a lot of fear about epilepsy that gets transferred onto the person affected by it. Some people have been taught to be very fearful of their fits and not to feel they have any kind of control over their condition. Your body suddenly goes out of your voluntary control so it's quite distressing. Many people have had a lot of teaching about how they've got to be very, very assiduous about taking their pills and worry about the level of drugs in their blood and things like that. You can easily get quite obsessional with those sorts of details in your life and so the epilepsy almost becomes the only thing in your life, rather than it being an aspect of your life. Some people really seem to spend their entire life thinking about the medical aspect of their condition. Again, it's not unique to people with epilepsy. Some people with other conditions make their physical condition almost their hobby. A certain way of living can prevent you from doing all sorts of things because worry, anxiety and fear are always top of your agenda.

I don't think my own personal sense of worth is affected one way or another. I know that probably sounds arrogant, as if you experience discrimination on a daily basis for a long time, it's very hard to keep your self-esteem going. The generalized discrimination that people with epilepsy feel or experience can actually knock down your self-esteem. Having said that, working in the disability movement, you don't get that problem on a daily basis and so what I get reflected back to me on a daily basis may be people complaining about me for other reasons, but it's not putting me down because I have fits.

Finally, I think it is important to be able to see what's funny and to make jokes. The best person that I know for that is Allan Sutherland who is a writer and comedian. I've certainly found it wonderful to hear Allan talking about the funny side of what's happened to him through his epilepsy. Often it's not funny when it happens: being approached by drunks in the street when you're hanging on to a lamppost just after you've had a fit is not actually funny at the time. But Allan makes it extraordinarily funny in retrospect, and that's just a part of not taking it all too seriously. Disability culture is a very important part of building the disability movement. It's having a different angle on what happens to us, a different angle on our conditions, and moving away from the standard cultural norm which is the 'tragic but brave' stereotype of disabled people. Everything that's different to that – which includes laughing at ourselves because those things are funny in retrospect – is all good.

Jane Avery

Jane Avery is a teacher and has had epilepsy since she was eight.

Different conditions, like fluctuating stress, do affect me. Stress is the thing that brings on my fits. I can't really prove it and I've charted my menstrual cycle, all those sort of things, trying to work out when I have fits, and it seems that I'm more likely to have a fit if I am ill or if I am under stress. Often I don't actually recognize at the time that stress is building up, but it's almost like a release valve. Maybe I'm not very good at dealing with the tension or the stresses, and so I let things build up and maybe not talk about things or whatever, and then off I go.

I have a *grand mal* fit (tonic-clonic seizure). I get some warning, an aura. I wake up in the morning and have little auras. It's a very strange sensation of feeling quite petrified, quite scared, and it's a kind of feeling that I don't experience at any other time. It's an anxiety but it's one that I don't experience normally. That might be for twenty seconds, something like that. Then I start getting up and I'll have another little one for thirty seconds or something, and I know that during the day, if I go to work and stress myself out, I'll have a fit. I can stay at home and maybe lie on the bed, listen to the radio, be completely relaxed and sleep, I nowadays might not necessarily have a fit, because I've kept myself quite calm. But it's guaranteed that if I go to work, I'd have a fit. So on the whole I ring in and I say that I'm not going to be in today.

Sometimes it's quite difficult because I'll go in the next day and they'll

say 'You were ill yesterday?' and I can't actually say 'Well, I was ill yesterday', because by staying at home I wasn't. I didn't actually have a fit, so
maybe I'm a bit economical with the truth sometimes. The day at home
goes down as a sick day. I have a card to fill in, an absence card. I'll probably have a bad day, say, every five or six weeks, something like that. This
term I've had three days off because of my epilepsy. If I'm lucky it falls at
the weekend – or unlucky, depending on which way you want to look at
it.

I live alone, without any particular concern. I've lived here for eight
years. At first I had a friend of mine living with me, then she moved out
and a guy who I was with lived here for three years. I asked him to move
out and I've had the flat by myself for the last couple of years. Because I
know when I'm going to have a fit, I can stay in bed and make myself safe.
If I was to wake up having had a fit, then so what? But it was quite nice
when Alice, who used to live upstairs, would pop by. It was nice to have
somebody around so that I could say 'I'm feeling terrible, will you go and
make me a cup of tea?', and stuff, but I survive on my own and I actually
enjoy it. I probably quite relish my independence, because people like the
British Epilepsy Association say you shouldn't take a bath on your own,
and certainly not live on your own, so it's kind of, almost, up yours!

I've never felt intimidated by epilepsy. I can feel frightened, it can
create a feeling of fear, but it doesn't frighten me that I have a fit. However, maybe going into teaching, going into the public sector, where
employment was regulated, was about feeling safer there. I felt comfortable going into teaching because I knew that they were into equal
opportunities, they were positive about people with disabilities and certainly, initially, it was nice to be in an environment where I didn't have to
fight. People were saying, 'Yes, it's okay you have epilepsy, that's fine,
it's not a problem.' Whereas – it's more my worry and it's not necessarily
based on any facts – perhaps if I'd gone into another working environment, it might have been less sympathetic. So I chose teaching partly
because it was likely to be a more sympathetic environment.

I tend to over-compensate for my epilepsy in terms of work. Every time
I take a day off, I get well again. On the one hand I'm thinking, 'Well,
this is my right and if I'm ill, I'm ill', but on the other hand I'm thinking, 'Oh hell, I should be at work and if I didn't have epilepsy I'd be
there. I probably do make more effort in my work and perhaps do more,
which in the end becomes counter-productive because I probably get more

tired than perhaps other people do, and in turn end up being more vulnerable to having a fit.

The reason I'm doing all that over-compensating is because I'm worried what other people think. If somebody came up to me and metaphorically put their arm round me and said, 'Look, it's no problem if you take your six days off a year, or whatever, because of your epilepsy, and we really do mean that,' then perhaps I would relax into that. But it's not like that, and I think it's getting tighter.

When I left university, in 1985, I did various jobs in the commercial world, and to be fair I never encountered any problem with regard to my epilepsy, although the company I worked for for three years was very small and so everything worked on a very personal level. There were only five or six of us and so perhaps you were more likely to be treated as an individual and your idiosyncrasies made allowances for. When I had to lie on the floor and have a fit, that was no problem. I had it all explained to me – exactly what I'd done – and they all thought it was a bit of a laugh, so that was fine. Apparently, I arched my back so that I was on the tip of my toes and the back of my head. God, I don't know how I did it.

Then I just got really hacked off with the commercial world and it really seemed a waste of time, but maybe that was more about me personally than anything else and I thought, well, what's the point? For one reason or another I ended up being seduced into the idea of going off and being a primary school teacher so I went and did a PCGE, the Post Graduate Certificate of Education, for a year over at the West London Institute. I used to cycle ten miles over there, ten miles back again, on my bike in the traffic, every day. I was so fit! It's about two miles now to work, not so good for my fitness, but anyway in the traffic and doing all the sort of things that the BEA would not advise.

My first job was in Tower Hamlets and the head teacher was good. She said 'Yes, okay, if you're feeling bad with your epilepsy, that's fine, off you go.' This is after the Inner London Education Authority was disbanded and budgets were delegated down to the boroughs. Each head was not, at that stage, responsible for things like salaries so perhaps absences and that sort of thing weren't such a big deal, and perhaps attitudes were more humanitarian. If you had a fit, that was fine. You went home and 'We're into equal opportunities, hey, hey, hey, and we don't mind.'

Gradually, probably over the last year or so, because it's since last September that they've had what they call local management of schools, each school has its own budget. Gradually schools have started to become more and more interested in why you've taken a day off, and you'll have a little record card and you will have to write on it why you took that day off, and sign it. Each time you have a day off you know that the next day you'll be presented with that card and you'll see your days totting up. It's quite insidious. It makes you feel 'Shit. Have I really had that many days off already?' Nothing's actually said, but equally, there's no feedback to say it's not a problem. There's been a big effort, certainly at my school, to reduce absences and it's obviously been somewhere that's been targeted in the budget, that's costing a lot, paying a lot to supply teachers and, 'Ho, ho, ho, wouldn't it be better if we tried to tighten up on the staff and encourage them not to take so many days off sick.' I feel quite threatened by it because even though I know that perhaps I'm one of those people who doesn't take a lot of days off sick, if you take out the days for my epilepsy. However, if you put those days in, then it becomes a huge total, so I do find it worrying, and there is no law on your side.

My last job was a maternity post – covering for somebody who was off on maternity leave – and it was two terms. When I was offered the job at the interview I said I was interested but what was the likelihood of it becoming a permanent post. And I was told, 'Well, we can't guarantee you the job but, frankly, once you're in the job, it's ninety-nine per cent yours. We'll have to re-advertise it, and you'll have to be re-interviewed, but if you've done two terms with us, it's yours in all but letter. That was January to July.

In the last couple of years, or year and a half, maybe, I've been seeing a new doctor at St Thomas's. Because my fits weren't particularly well controlled, he asked me if I wanted to consider exploring new drugs, and I said yes. So I went to this new school in Dulwich, knowing that I was likely to chop and change my pills, but I wasn't going to tell them that. As it worked out, I probably took quite a lot of days off. I think it was ten days off in two terms, but four of those were nothing to do with my epilepsy. When it came round to them re-advertising the job or the governors talking about it, I was invited for a little informal chat. They asked me whether I would like to consider extending my temporary contract because I'd happened to let slip the fact that my drugs had been changed and had taken the head teacher into my confidence. She was saying, 'Well, I know that your drugs have been chopped and changed and that interviews are stressful things. We could extend your temporary contract and you wouldn't have to be interviewed. Then, in a couple of terms, say, we could re-advertise the job and you'd be feeling so much better.' I got quite shirty about it and said 'Look, the situation was, two terms and then you've got to re-advertise the job.' I didn't say it, but in terms of the equal opportunities law, they had to do it. They quickly realized this and that idea suddenly disappeared. I was told that they were very sorry, but they had to re-advertise the job, and they were unable to offer it to me temporarily for the next two terms so I would have to reapply. I thought, fine. When it came round to being interviewed, I probably said much the same sort of things as I'd said the last time, but I was told that they were offering the job to somebody else, who was newly qualified.

The thing that underlay it, I felt, was they didn't want to take me on permanently, knowing, or not knowing what the situation was going to be long term with regard to my epilepsy. Was I going to have as many days off as I was having, which was only two, three days a term, or was it going to get better, or was it going to get worse? And I believe that they weren't willing to accept the fact that I might take extra days off because of my epilepsy. I couldn't prove it. There's no way I could prove it.

I've always been a bit of fighter. I was eight when I was diagnosed. Both my parents were very good about it. They didn't let it interfere. I don't think my Dad was particularly interested in me or my brother when we were children, and he only allowed my mother to have children because she particularly wanted to and he knew he didn't really have much say in the matter. She was a nurse at St Thomas's for about ten years, (she didn't get married until she was twenty-eight) and so she had no problem with my epilepsy. I think probably both of them were quite traumatized by the fact that I had epilepsy, but they certainly didn't stop me doing anything. They were very determined that I should have a completely normal life and so I was allowed to do anything I wanted to. I've never been denied doing anything.

Consequently, I have always been out about my epilepsy. I had a bit of a reaction against it when I was first at college, when I did my BSc. I didn't take my pills for two years, not having had a fit for about eleven years and being convinced that I didn't have epilepsy and that there was nothing wrong with me. My mum used to say to me every so often 'Look, it's your life, but I would advise you to go and see the doctor.' I knew that if I went to see the doctor, he would say 'Take the pills.' So I didn't go, and eventually I did have a fit again. It hasn't really stabilised since. I suppose I'm more open about it than ever before, perhaps because it impinges more on my life now because I actually have fits.

When I was young, I used to take Phenytoin. It makes you very aggressive. My dad is one of those people who is extremely self-centred. He's a very nice man, but he's extremely self-centred. He didn't like children and as far as my parents were concerned, I was extremely self-centred as well. I used to fight with them all the time. I would never give in to him and I considered him completely unreasonable. I had huge tantrums, way beyond the terrible twos and threes. In retrospect I think that a lot of that was probably due to the Phenytoin. I went back on Phenytoin briefly a couple of years ago and had two incredible tantrums with the head of the school I taught at in Tower Hamlets. I think she was completely shocked because I'd been so placid for two years before that, and suddenly there I was telling her where to go. She actually came up and apologised to me after both of these incidents so she obviously carried the guilt. I never discussed this with my parents, or with my mum, and in fact when I went back on Phenytoin, I had another huge argument with my dad. Suddenly, having been off it for three, four, five years and then gone back on it, everybody saw that the person I was on Phenytoin the second time around was the person that I had been when I was much younger. Nobody had told my parents to look out for it; nobody had told me that I might react to it in that way and I probably went through a lot of my adolescence not relating to people particularly well and assuming that it was my fault. And in actual fact I don't think an awful lot of it was my fault. I think perhaps it was, quite a lot, the fault of the pills. They were making me angry all the time.

I did my spate of therapy in the 1980s. I got into it because I did hit a very low ebb, and I think my self esteem was appallingly low right through my adolescence. There were little bits in between which were okay, but they were all very much based on what other people thought. I think there's still a lot of that in me. Maybe you can't leave that completely, but I'm certainly more calm about myself and more accepting of myself than I was. I used to hate the fact that I'd have these incredible arguments with people, be it my dad, or friends. I was at boarding school for a while, and there are people who I'm still great friends with but who I had a few real arguments with. In retrospect, the whole thing was about tension that was so pent up it just kind of exploded. It could have been about anything. It was just about day-to-day things that were difficult to cope with when I was taking Phenytoin. Now I'm not taking it, I'm able to cope. It just made me very aggressive. I think there's quite an aggressive streak in me anyway, but maybe everyone has one and the drug preyed on it and built it up.

When I went to college, as I said, I stopped taking my pills for two, three years, didn't have a fit, and then aged twenty-two, twenty-three, something like that, had a fit and vaguely started taking the Phenytoin again. I kept forgetting, didn't take it very seriously and then decided that the doctor at St Thomas's was not much good. My mum can remember him being there when she was a nurse, which meant that he'd been there for at least twenty or thirty years. I decided I'd really had it up to here with him, so I went to my GP and got referred to the National Hospital. I would turn up there and see a different doctor every time. They took me off Phenytoin, put me on Tegretol, and it used to make me really, really tired. I would take about half the amount I was supposed to take, and go back there every time and say, 'Look, I can't take what you tell me to take, it makes me too tired. Do something about it.' And they said, 'No, don't worry. If you just take these drugs you'll be fine.' So I did that for probably two or three years.

Then I changed GPs and my new GP said there was now a new doctor at St Thomas's, and did I want to go and see him? So I went back to St Thomas's and now I have a very good doctor who is probably about the same age as me. He is keen on establishing himself and he puts himself out to help me and he said, 'Well, you know, we'll run through the drugs as quickly or as slowly as you want. If you want to try new ones, we'll try new ones; if you don't want to, we won't.' So I've kind of led the pace.

He's kept me on a little bit of Tegretol but I'm also taking Clovozan, which are the 'blue bombers'. They are lovely; they make you feel really calm, and they're actually very good. I told my mother about their lovely side-effects and she was very puritanical about it. I said, 'For heaven's sake! You allowed me to take drugs that made me feel hideous for ten, eleven years, and now I get a drug that actually makes me feel good and you're saying to me I shouldn't take it?' I like taking them, really, because they're nice to suck and make you feel good. I'm not sure what they do for my fits but, to be fair, I think that, as far as I can gather, if I have a grand mal fit, they've made them shorter. Paul, my boyfriend, remembers the first fit I had with him which was before I was taking the pills I have now. It probably lasted about three minutes, and it was an 'Exorcist-eat-your-heart-out' kind of job. Apparently now they're maybe a minute, something like that, and they're much less severe.

I've just started taking another drug, on top of it all, because the philosophy seems to be that we add before we start taking away. I'm a little bit uncomfortable about this, I feel I'm taking a cocktail of drugs. Anyway, now I have a very new drug called Gabbapentin as well, so I'm taking Tegretol, which makes me drowsy, Clovozan and the Gabbapentin. I haven't really been taking Gabbapentin long enough to know how it affects me but you're supposed to be able to take six a day. I'm now taking two a day, but if I take three, they just make me feel very dizzy and completely spaced out, so I think I'm quite sensitive to all these drugs. The only thing that I'm really hacked off about is that the one drug I really want to stop taking is the Tegretol, I'm on a small dose of that, 500mg a day, but I'm just dying to stop taking it. Maybe I should just pour them away or just not take them. I've had it up to here.

I suppose I go out of the way to tell people I have epilepsy because I feel quite determined that people need educating about it. That is very paternal isn't it, very patronizing, but the majority of people don't know very much about what epilepsy is and so I tell people, probably more than I need to. Most people are actually curious, and they actually want to know what it's all about. Being quite egocentric, I'm quite happy to talk bout myself for half an hour if they want to listen. Sometimes if I get pity I tend to really push it away, and maybe I'm still a little bit aggressive towards that. Often that's people's first reaction: 'Oh, that must be so hard to cope with.' 'For the majority of days I'm just like you,' I say, 'and I would far rather have epilepsy than, say, ME which would affect me every day.' That's the kind of thing I would say to people. I feel a bit sorry for myself once every six or seven weeks but otherwise I don't. I could take someone's pity over the fact that I don't have a driving licence and I can't drive any more. Now that would be legitimate pity, but actual pity for the epilepsy, I don't really have very much time for.

That sounds very hard hearted but you do get frustrated by people's often prurient interest. There's a sense of people wanting their fears to be taken away by us. They want to be told what to do if we have a fit. I do get a bit frustrated about that, I must admit, because to me it's obvious what you do: you just don't do anything. If they said to me, 'As far as I know, this is what I should do; X, Y, Z,' then I'd probably respond much more positively than the slightly pathetic one, 'What do we do when you have a fit?' My first reaction is, that it's very, very unlikely that I'm going to have a fit in front of you because I know when I wake up in the morning if I'm likely to have a fit. It's almost, well a 'Bog off, Leave me alone' kind of feeling I get when someone says that.

I've had that with the head at school. She's said to me, 'What would we do if you had a fit?' On the one hand, it was all very well placed and the rest of it, but it's a bit too well meaning. The school, where I worked is a state primary school with an extremely exclusive catchment area and a load of parents with very high expectations for their children. The head was probably completely terrified of most of the parents and instead of having the courage to stand up to them, she tended to play to them. I was talking to her one day about my epilepsy and I was saying that I'm always so open about it that at some point I would like to talk to the children about the fact that I have epilepsy. I think it's a good thing for children to be aware of the fact that people with epilepsy are just like anybody else. At this point the woman flinched with fear. She said that she really didn't feel that this was appropriate and that children would tell their parents who might misunderstand. She felt that it was far better that I didn't tell the parents, or the children. My feeling was the parents had the right to know their children were being taught by somebody with epilepsy, and if they had a problem they could come and talk to me and I would be quite happy to talk to them. As far as I was concerned it was not a problem and if they needed sorting out then I would have been quite happy to help them sort it out. However I was on the two-term temporary contract, so feeling a bit prudent I felt, 'Right, I'll work my two terms of temporary contract, get my permanent contract and then I will kick off.' But of course it didn't come to that, and so that was a situation where epilepsy was dealt with negatively. It's one example of the prejudice that's around.

I think people still are slightly uncomfortable about it; the very fact that they'll ask you what they should do if you have a fit. They're scared of it, they don't understand it. Nobody's out there explaining that it's not a problem. Most people have no understanding or experience and maybe there is still a sort of medieval view about epilepsy. The demons are still alive and well, but maybe in a slightly different form. People would like to say, 'Oh yes, we feel fine about epilepsy,' but they aren't. There's a stigma with it and there's a kind of real discrimination against people with epilepsy.

When I was growing up, I wouldn't have described myself as the same as other people with other disabilities, but nowadays I would. Many people would be shocked by that. Some people would say well you're not disabled, you've just got epilepsy. British Rail think we're disabled: you can get a disabled rail card. Because you're likely to be unable to drive, it was taken within the umbrella of disability. Probably the majority of people wouldn't consider it a disability but I think perhaps there is a strength in the disabled lobby in the same way as there's a strength in the women's lobby or the anti-racist lobby or whatever, and perhaps for that reason I would consider myself disabled because I feel quite strongly that not only people with epilepsy but anybody with any disability has as many rights as anybody else. It's more about finding a place for myself. I am interested in the issue of rights for disabled people, but I don't like the idea of considering myself to be disabled. My gut reaction is that I don't want to be disabled because I feel some stigma attached to that, but my head says that it is probably the strongest group for me to consider myself part of. In a sense the easy option is to say I have epilepsy and it's no big deal and I'm just like anybody else, but the reality is that having epilepsy is considered a disability by the majority of the population and as such, perhaps I'd do well to put myself in that group.

That said, I would be interested in having a cure for my condition. If somebody says to me, 'There's an operation: it's 99 per cent certain; there's only 1 per cent chance of it not going away. There's no chance of it making you worse, so there's 99 per cent chance you're going to get completely rid of your epilepsy. Do you want to have this chance? It's free,' then yes, I'm up for it. I've talked with my doctor about several things – surgery for example – and his response was that there are a lot of other drugs that we haven't tried. I would like not to have fits because when I do have them it makes me feel oh, so desperately anxious and sad and morose. Just the way that it makes me feel emotionally is so painful that to be rid of that would be really positive. Maybe if I had fits and didn't have all those feelings as well, I'd be happy to live with the fits, but I don't like the feelings that are associated with the fits. When I was younger, I would go straight into the fits, just like that, so I didn't have those feelings and in a sense maybe that was easier. From a personal point of view, I would be quite happy to be rid of my fits.

I suppose the only thing I get really hacked off with is the business of not being allowed to drive. In terms of my quality of life, I'd love to drive. I did drive for a while, for about five years. Not being able to drive now, you suddenly realize how geared the whole world is to driving. Because I know when I'm going to have a fit, I could drive quite happily. I feel it's a kind of injustice; the system works against me. I'd be very tempted to try to drive if I thought that my memory wouldn't be any worse by having fits. I'd probably be very tempted not to take the drugs and tell everybody that I wasn't having fits and get a driving licence again. But I know that my memory does get so much worse when I'm having fits. There's no way that I would have a fit at the wheel because I just know if I'm going to have a bad day. I wouldn't drive in the same way I wouldn't ride my bike. There's no law against me riding my bike and I'm probably in a much more dangerous situation, much more vulnerable than in a car, and I do feel angry about that. I can get really quite angry about it, really really angry, because it's just taken away so much in terms of my life.

I haven't driven for the last three or four years now. I couldn't live out-side London and have anything like a decent social life. I live in London partly because I like being here, but maybe I've stayed here longer than I might have done because the public transport system is virtually non-existent once you get outside London, because you haven't got shops on your doorstep and all that kind of thing. I suppose I'm lucky because I have long-suffering friends who take me to Sainsbury's and things like that, all the exciting things. Going to the supermarket becomes a real luxury, not to be taken lightly. Although I have my independence and I live here on my own, I lost a lot in terms of my independence when I stopped driving: things like just being able to go out and go and see somebody for an hour or so. I don't go out during the week really at all because it's such a big deal. For me, to hop in a car to go and see some-body for half an hour, turn round and come back again, is a distant story.

Alison Lawson

Alison Lawson is a Trouble Shooter Manager for a Recruitment Consultancy and is currently studying for an MBA. She was diagnosed as having epilepsy about five years ago.

I don't know what brings on my seizures. I just black out. I don't usually have any warning and it just feels to me as if I've fainted. It can be for a very long time, up to a couple of hours. I don't see anything, I'm completely passed out. Apparently I'm actually not unconscious but it seems that way to me. So for me a seizure is just that I completely black out, fall to the floor and do nothing at all for the whole period of time, which can be anything from ten minutes up to a couple of hours. Then at the end of that period when I wake up I have about ten or fifteen minutes where I'm not altogether with it because some people may be saying my name and I won't be able to answer. When I fully come round I feel as if I'm very hung over, and I just need to go to bed to sleep for the rest of the day.

I tell people they need to check that when I've fallen I haven't obviously hurt myself on the way down. Other than that they just need to try and keep me warm, to keep an eye on my colour to make sure I'm not going blue, and to leave me completely. If they are concerned then obviously they can call a doctor after a while but there is no need to at all. The main thing is not to worry. Despite that, ambulances do play a large part in my life. I've seen them a lot. All of the ambulance people who come have always said, 'There's not really any need for us to come here, but if you're

ever worried please tell everybody that it's fine to call.' That's very re-
assuring because I think it's worse for the people who are watching me
have a seizure than it is for me. Luckily, most of the attacks or fits I've had
have been at work. I'm able to tell people in advance that I'm epileptic
and I've written down what they need to know so there should be less need
for them to worry or panic. They still do worry, and it's one thing saying I
might just fall over, and it's another thing when you hear a clunk on the
desk and there I am passed out.

There is a funny story about before I was actually diagnosed as epileptic
but was starting to have fits. The office I worked in was two floors up and
an applicant came in and said to one of my colleagues, 'I don't know if I
should tell you but there's somebody collapsed at the bottom of the stairs.'
And they said, 'Oh don't worry that's just Alison.' I think the applicant
was probably a bit concerned and somebody did come downstairs and pull
me up to somewhere more comfortable. I often think it was quite funny.

I have wondered about whether people seeing somebody like me in
authority having a seizure, feel it undermines my status, my managerial
position, but I don't think it does. I did worry about it for a while but
now I feel it's a fact of my life. It doesn't affect the way I do my job and
therefore it shouldn't affect how I'm viewed as part of my work. I make
sure I tell people as soon as they're working for me, not within the first
five minutes but certainly in the first day so that they are aware of it. And
then usually everything's fine.

I have seizures reasonably frequently. It can vary from anything up to
maybe three or four times a week and probably down to maybe once every
three or four weeks, but it's never very, very severe. Before I was diagnosed I was having seizures quite regularly and that was quite bad. On a
busy week, a pressured week, I could have four seizures, and that could
cause problems. Obviously, I have to try and make sure that I do everything I can so that I don't have the seizures. I know for me the worse thing
is being overtired. If I am feeling tired and I don't go to bed, perhaps if
I'm out and I think, 'Oh well, I'd rather stay,' then I'm much more likely
to have a seizure and then have to have a day off work. So, to a certain
degree, I'm in control of them.

I don't feel guilty about the inconvenience at work of my seizures or the
disruption of having to go home. I did feel very guilty initially up until
really the last two or three months when I realized that I had a lot of support from the senior management in the company. Up until then I was

thinking, 'It's very inconvenient for the branch at the time. It's probably setting a bad example. Will I loose my job? Will they think less of me? Will I loose my seniority?' Then I realised that everybody was behind me at work and they were saying, 'Well, there's nothing to feel guilty about. Your health is the most important thing. If you're feeling guilty about it and worrying you're more likely to have more seizures, so we'd rather that you didn't worry about it and relax, and if you have to have a day off, two days off, then fine, just have the time off.' So I no longer need to feel guilty now.

There was a stage, earlier this year, when I was having a lot of seizures. When I get up in the morning I often feel as if I'm likely to have a seizure. I was going through a stage of thinking, 'Well, do I feel as if I am going to have a seizure, or I am likely to have a seizure? I feel well enough to go into work right now, so I'll go in.' Then something would happen and I would have a seizure. I would have to go home, and somebody would have to come home with me, so it was taking two people away from their work. My manager said, 'It would really be a lot better, if you feel that you're going to have a seizure in the morning, if you didn't come in. Because if you come in and have a seizure you're actually taking two people away from the work; yourself and the other person, rather than just you, so it's just one day out.' And even though that may sound rather harsh, I actually found it made me feel a lot more relaxed about it because I thought, 'Well yes, it's true.' It does actually make it worse if I'm going in, sort of struggling in and putting a brave face on it and having a fit and hoping that they'll be fine about it as well. I'm not insecure about my job, but I do perhaps make myself work a bit harder to make up for it. That's the only way I do, the only way feel I have to. Unlike with any other illness or problems one might have, say if I didn't have epilepsy I might think, 'I don't think I'll go in today because I don't feel that well.' Whereas I feel that it's important for me to go in all the other times I possibly can, so that they know that I'm not milking the fact that I'm having the time off, so that they know that it's completely genuine. That way, when I have the time off, I'm having the time off because I really do need it. So that's really the only way. Other than that, I just feel that I want to be able to do my job to the same level that I did it before, which I can and I'm allowed to.

I was very surprised when I discovered I had epilepsy. I found it hard, in one sense. My family in particular kept saying, 'How can you be epileptic? Nobody in the family ever has been, and how come you're twenty-five and it's just been diagnosed now?' I found that it was quite difficult to get information about it. For instance, in the library, it was impossible to get books on epilepsy to read up and find out why I might have suddenly appeared with it now. But I didn't feel alarmed about it, I don't think. I certainly don't remember that I was scared about it.

For a time there were a lot of negative reactions around. Not in terms of them feeling very shocked, an 'Oh, that's awful!' type of reaction. It was more in terms of 'How can she have been epileptic? I don't understand how this can have happened, and I wonder if the doctors have checked everything they need to have checked.' This didn't actually make me feel any better at all, because I didn't really want people to be saying, 'Oh well, that can't be right. It must be something else, or it must be something more serious.' I really wanted people to accept that if I was epileptic, then I was epileptic and okay, let's just get on with it now rather than argue with it. I don't feel that having epilepsy is a tragedy in any sense at all. I think that without being trite there are an awful lot worse things to have. I mean, I can get on with my life to a large degree. I'd obviously much rather I didn't have it, but of all the things that one could have, it's something that I can live with. A doctor of mine also said quite a reasonable thing: that most people, at some stage of their life, have something, some illness or condition which could be lifestyle related, if you like. I think what he meant was that maybe somebody gets to middle age and has a heart attack, and they have to change their lifestyle to survive. With epilepsy, I have to adapt my lifestyle to a certain degree to be healthier because that's going to make me less likely to have seizures, but it's not a huge change. So I'd rather know about it now and be able to do something about it than have a heart attack at fifty and have much less time to do something about it.

To some extent, in certain areas, I do adapt my life to suit the condition. This is primarily in making sure that I get adequate sleep. It feels so boring when you think, 'I can't go out tonight because I'm really not too well, I'm feeling a bit borderline.' Or I go out and say 'I have to go home now,' although I'd much rather be carrying on having a good time.' Domestically, it has meant that my husband, in order for me to get rest, had to start doing all the housework. That was hard for him, because he was not what you would consider a 'new man'. So that was quite a drastic change. It also meant I had to change my plans: I was due to start an MBA course that September, I had to seriously consider whether I would be able to do that because of the extra work and the extra pressure, but I went ahead and did it and it's been fine. I've stopped drinking, and although it's hardly the end of the world, I'd much rather be able to have a glass of wine when I wanted to. But it makes me much more likely to have a seizure, and I feel awful when I've had just a couple of drinks. I think those are probably the major changes I've made.

I'm not going to go to the umpteenth degree and make my life un-livable. I don't, for example, keep the bathroom door unlocked either just in case anything happens. I don't think that I'm being reckless but I sup-pose I think, 'Well, I'll do what I have to do; live on my own terms, I don't want to live what other people think is the safest possible life for me. I'm not going to be reckless, but I don't think I'm living a dangerous life. I know that, for instance, I'm not supposed to go parachute jumping or scuba diving. Until I knew that I couldn't do them neither particularly appealed, anyway. But I don't think that I shouldn't necessarily do them. There are dangers in everything. I don't think it's any good to go around wrapped up in cotton wool. I was concerned, especially initially, when I was having seizures at the side of the London Underground platforms. I fell down stairs because I had a seizure at the top of the stairs and those things obviously bothered me. However, now that the condition is start-ing to be under control and predictable, I don't feel that I need to take much more care than anybody else.

I'm not sure how other people, who don't know me, react to me having a seizure in a public place such as a tube station. I don't know because ob-viously I was blacked out, for want of better words. I didn't really know how people reacted. Usually, all I knew was when I was waking up in an ambulance or in an accident and emergency room at hospital. I accept that they always always called an ambulance straight away and were obviously concerned. Mostly when I have them I'm with people that I know, and after a while I get used to it. I also keep a note inside my handbag that says, 'I am epileptic. This is what to do.' And people did. I did worry about it a little but I thought, 'Well, it's all in public places. If I collapse I'll have to be fairly unlucky to collapse next to somebody who's going to be dishonest enough to mug me while there are a lot of people round as well.' I suppose that's a benefit of travelling on the Central Line; you're not likely to be far from any other people.

Considering other changes to my lifestyle, to be frank, pregnancy is not something I've particularly given a lot of thought to. The only consideration I've given at the moment — because it's not something I'm planning immediately — is how it would affect me in pregnancy. I know that there can be a lot of problems because of the hormone changes and your reactions to medication, and that bothers me in that I'm concerned that I might have to have a lot of time off work. I might not be able to work up until the date that I would have like to have worked. I haven't really thought much further than that. Except, funnily enough, at the weekend I was with friends who recently had a baby. I was holding the baby and I thought, 'Wouldn't it be awful if I had a seizure now,' which of course it would have been. Then I thought about how that sort of thing could happen if it was a baby of my own. There is a whole idea you read in the manuals about how you should breast feed your child with a lot of cushions around you, in case you keel over or something. Well, as I say it's not something I've given an awful lot of thought to. But I would hope that I wouldn't have to do all that because obviously it would be very sad. It would make the whole experience fraught, rather than happy. But I honestly couldn't say that I have thought too much about it. I try not to look at just the black side ahead. Apart from anything else, I could be free of seizures totally by the time I decide to have a family, because I know these things can come and go. So it's something I'd rather not worry about right now. I'm not digging my head in the sand about it, but it's not something I'm overly worried about.

I was about to get married when I had the first seizure. I wasn't actually diagnosed for about two or three months, until about the Christmas after I got married in September. The major effect the epilepsy had on the marriage was to bring me and my husband closer together. I'm a very independent person generally, but I had to become quite dependent on him for quite a long period of time. Initially, I found that very difficult to cope with, but having to get used to being dependent on somebody made us closer. The major difference, of course, was that my husband took on a different role: he carried all the domestic chores. He actually decided to take a step down in his career to be able to do that. To allow me to carry on my job and start doing the MBA was very important to me. So, because he made a choice, to give up a stage of his career for me, made me feel really important to him.

I don't think it would have affected our decision to get married if he and I had found out earlier about the epilepsy. He's very pragmatic and would think, 'Well, we'll get over that,' rather than seeing it as a major hurdle.

I hadn't really thought of epilepsy as a disability until recently because I'd just thought 'Well it is there and I'll just have to get on with it.' But I suppose it is a disability because it can stop you from doing quite a lot of things. I wouldn't say that I was disabled. Maybe that's just the way I feel. I've just got to live with it in the same way as I lived before. I spoke earlier about the example of somebody having a heart attack in middle age. I don't know if that would be considered a disability, but it certainly has an effect on how you live your life.

I haven't spent a lot of time getting involved in issues surrounding epilepsy as a whole, because, as I said, I just want to get on and live my life. I did think about joining a group at one stage because I got some help from British Epilepsy Association, but it's something I haven't really got round to. I suppose, for that reason it's something that is obviously not that important to me. Not because I don't want to stand up and say 'I'm epileptic' because I'm perfectly happy to do that, but I don't know that I particularly feel that I would get any support, or that I need any support from the group. However, I found it so surprising that when I tried to get information from libraries about epilepsy, I could have got thirty books on diabetes or multiple sclerosis or all sorts of things, but I couldn't get a single one on epilepsy, which I thought was a bit surprising, to say the least, especially when it's such a relatively common condition. It was almost as if I was asking about something that was very rare. So from that point of view I think that it probably needs its visibility heightening, so to speak. I don't know when it is, but there's Epilepsy Week. I remember seeing it in the papers last year. It was always the same: the things that were brought up were always about people who were very severe epileptics. Obviously, that's got a much greater effect on your life but I think it's still important that people know all about epilepsy and how it affects people such as me, which is not in a major, major way, but it still affects my life.

I think that desperately trying to prove you are normal, or don't have epilepsy, is a bad thing. I can understand somebody doing it, although I don't agree with that because it's putting the person into the category of, again, epilepsy is something you don't want to have, or 'Oh dear, that's something bad!' It isn't at all and you don't need to be worried about it. I don't think you need to be worried about whether it's a disability or not because it just is. Whatever you want to call it, it is just there, so I don't think it's something you should fight against and say, 'Well, you know, I'm fighting to be normal.' You just are what you are.

I don't feel that anti-discrimination legislation would necessarily be effective for disabled people and epilepsy in particular. In my job I see a lot of the results of other legislation against discrimination – for race equality and sex equality – and I find that there are always people, in fact a surprisingly high number of people, that want to get around that legislation. If they feel strongly, for instance, that only a woman could do this job because it's very mundane, then the legislation won't change their mind. What is more important is to change people's views on whatever you're trying to legislate against. In this instance it's more important to change people's views on how easy it is to employ somebody who is epileptic, that it's not going to be a major problem at all. So, rather than introducing legislation I would, personally, look at changing people's minds, changing people's views.

I haven't as yet tried to educate the employers I come into contact with. If the issue came up in terms of somebody being epileptic, it wouldn't be a problem. But in actual fact I don't think I would be in a position to be educating people, because I wouldn't necessarily know that somebody was epileptic. If I was putting them forward to a client or knew of them being sent to a client, it wouldn't be something I'd have to mention to the client, because if somebody comes to us to look for work through us, they don't need to say that they are epileptic. Unless they have put down that they had a significantly long period off work, and we followed that up, I don't think that that would come through at all. If somebody did tell me they had epilepsy, I wouldn't have to disclose it to the employer, nor would I go out of my way to hide it, but I wouldn't bring it to their attention. I don't think that that is really up to me to do. It's between the client and the person who is looking for a job.

I don't hide it at all at work. In fact, at work and with my friends and family, it's important that people know. While it's not the first thing that I do when I go up and meet somebody – I don't say 'Hi, I'm Alison, I'm epileptic,' – it is something that I'm quite keen on, to tell people, fairly quickly. It's not just so that they know what to do if something happens, but so that they know that it doesn't mean that I'm – you know – foaming at the mouth, which is often the sort of thing that somebody will say. Or that something serious is going to happen to me or that it's seriously impairing my life. Having said that, a couple of years ago I applied for another job. I was offered the job and then had to go through the stage of having a medical. I was finding it very difficult to decide whether to say at this stage, that I was epileptic or not. It was also a job that involved driving quite a lot and so I wondered whether that would make the company think twice about keeping the offer or rescinding it. As with all offers, it was subject to a medical and I found it very difficult decision to make. In the end I didn't actually take the job which wasn't in any way related to my decision, or indecision I should say, about disclosing the epilepsy, but it was a very difficult decision. I don't know what I would have done really.

At the moment, I'm responsible for a team of staff in a branch and the success of the branch. I spend a few months at a time going from branch to branch, going into whichever branch is doing particularly badly, that's struggling. I go in and decide what the problem is, and start putting them right, hopefully. During that time I have the responsibility for the team. I think I'm good at my job. I'm lucky I was in a fortunate position in that when I was offered the other job, where I had to have the medical, I was asked to stay with my present company and that was when I was given this position as trouble shooter manager which I really enjoy. The fact that the company is sponsoring me to do an MBA means that obviously they feel happy with my work. I really enjoy it and I think that's half of it. I don't think it's my abilities that override any concern by my employers about my epilepsy. Having seen the reaction from them, I think they would make as much of an effort to keep on somebody who was average as they would to keep on somebody who was good. They have been genuinely concerned and feel that illness is, or whatever you want to call it, is something to be dealt with, something that you have to be sympathetic to, especially when it's a long-term illness. It's not a situation where you can say, 'Okay, well, go away, have a week off and come back and everything's okay.' I think that they would be actually sympathetic. All my company would be looking for is a commitment to the company by the person when fit and well. As with anything, if they felt somebody was taking advantage of the situation then they wouldn't be very keen to keep the person on, which is quite reasonable.

The only discrimination I have experienced, in areas apart from work, are in terms of insurance. The insurance premiums for, I think, mortgages, other household things and driving have been increased. I don't know whether you could really call that discrimination. I suppose that's fair enough. I wasn't too aware of the discrimination that other people face until early this year when I was having further problems myself. I was completely shocked to find out that there are certain categories of people who will lose their job if they've had two epileptic fits. My doctor was saying that, for instance, if a policeman or a teacher has one epileptic fit they can be put on a pension and retired out if they have another. I was really shocked at that; I think that's terrible. I can understand in a way that with a teacher, an educational authority is going to be concerned about the effect on the children if they're seeing the teacher unwell, very often. But it is a difficult illness to predict, especially as if you give somebody a little bit of time to adapt to it, they may well be able to get it under control. I think it's so unfair if people can either lose their jobs or not be given a job in the first place for something that might actually only take a few months to get under control and be fine. It is unfair because it is, I'm sure, based on complete misunderstanding of the condition. If people understood what can be done about it, how it affects somebody and how they can get it under control, I'm sure that they would no longer see the need to discriminate. Having said that I know that there are vast differences in degrees of it, and I know that for a lot of people it's very hard or impossible to control, but there's a vast number of people that aren't at that level.

I think my life would have been very different if I had been diagnosed with epilepsy at eight or nine. By having been diagnosed at twenty-five a lot of my life was in place, if you like. I'd decided on the type of career I wanted, I'd been through education to the level that I wanted at that stage, and I had a certain amount of confidence. If I'd been very much younger it would have been difficult to be as confident and to really think 'Well, what choices do I have? What do I want as a career?' I felt I could do anything. I would probably have felt limited if diagnosed as a child, but by the time I was diagnosed it was too late to feel limited because I was doing it already, so I'm very glad that I wasn't diagnosed then. Also, I think it would be very difficult for the parents. It must be very difficult for parents, relatives and friends alike to give the same freedoms to a child to experiment if they know that they have a problem.

I felt very very let down by the medical profession. In fact I feel very angry about it.

When I was first diagnosed I was referred to a consultant at one of the London hospitals. I only went a couple of times to see him because after that I felt that I wanted to say to him, 'Look, my epilepsy might not be very serious to you and I know you're dealing with a lot more serious cases all the time, but it's important to me and it's affecting my life,' because he was very patronizing and I felt that he just wasn't really concerned at all.' The side-effects of the medication I was having then were intolerable. I was constantly washed out, constantly depressed. Obviously that was affecting my life far more than the epilepsy was in the first place, and he didn't want to know.

I then went through a stage of the illness being under control. But earlier this year, and last year, when it became a problem again, I found that I was being fobbed off all the way down the line. It was very much a case of the doctor saying, or the consultant saying, 'There, there, never mind. Don't worry about it.' It actually got to the stage where I was ringing up all the time. I rang up one of the doctors one day and said, 'Look, think of it like this. If somebody was to say to you, "You're going to have to stop your career as a doctor and you're not going to be able to study, and actually you won't be able to have a social life," would you not think that that would be worrying you? It might not be the most important thing to you, but it is seriously affecting me.' I think that made him think a little bit, and then finally I had to see a doctor privately, when I felt that was the only way I was going to be able to get to somebody who would listen, as I was paying for their time. He did listen and explained to me a lot of the answers that I wanted, but up until then I had felt as though I was knocking my head against a brick wall; that nobody was interested and where could I go? That was when I contacted the British Epilepsy Association, because I just didn't know what else to do.

I think I was driving everybody mad. But it was at a time where I was actually finding it difficult to talk properly so I knew I wasn't getting my views over very coherently anyway and that bothered me. I'd get in to see a doctor and I'd be all psyched up. A couple of times I was so angry I was crying. I remember saying, crying and saying, 'Look I'm not a hysterical patient. I just want you to give me some answers and tell me this.' So I don't feel I had very good service from the medical profession at all. I have no idea why they handled me so badly. At the time I felt it was because my symptoms weren't very severe and so they probably thought that I was exaggerating.

It seems incredible that they're not more knowledgeable about such a common illness or condition and not more sympathetic. They certainly ought to be. Considering epilepsy has been around for years and years and years, it seems bizarre that so little is being done. It makes me feel very perplexed more than anything else. I can't understand it. I know that medical science is not able to find the answers to everything, but the only answer to questions such as 'What would have caused it?' 'Why did it only become apparent when I was 25?' – was 'We don't know. We don't know the answers to these things; it's still a mystery.' Surely there must be a lot to be gained by actually researching it, actually getting the answers. It seems incredible to me.

Society at large is still very ignorant about epilepsy and people are mis-informed. I suppose it's a chicken and egg situation really. Maybe there's still a taboo about it, so that people who are epileptic feel that they don't want to make it public, because of what people think of them. Yet by doing that, people aren't then able to eradicate the taboo because they don't know anybody who is both epileptic and fine. So it goes on. I think it will take more people to say, to sort of stand up and say, 'I'm epileptic and this is how it affects my life, and as you can see it's not something caused by me being mad or whatever.' People will be able to understand that, and it will progress from there. I thought epilepsy didn't make me angry but now I'm getting all heated.

I think that the majority of people make *me* feel that it's my problem and that I have to get on with it. But the people that are probably closest to me don't make me feel that way at all; my husband, my closest friends don't make me feel that way. For instance, if we're out for a drink, usually I'll say, 'No I'm not drinking', and they won't say, 'Oh good, you shouldn't drink at all.' Yet if I'm having a drink, people I know only vaguely or reasonably well, who know I have epilepsy, will say, 'Oh you shouldn't be drinking'. That is the sort of thing that I find a bit irritating because it's not actually helping. It's making me feel that I'm in the wrong for doing something, rather than actually managing the condition, and also it's not actually their business. I think most people, because they don't understand that much about it, would rather put the problems of it on to my shoulders because it's easier for them. But as I say, people who are closest to me don't at all so that makes it so much better for me.

People's reactions are funny. Often it's absolutely way out of proportion to the condition. I find it at work. I think that people automatically try not to react. As I have said I think it's important to tell people I work with, fairly quickly, that I have the condition. Usually what happens is I'll say, 'Oh, by the way, it's nothing to worry about, it's no big deal but I am epileptic. If I do pass out, in the back of my diary it says what to do.' They just say 'Okay, fine, fine, fine', and then a couple of days later they'll say, 'You know when you said you were epileptic. Well, what does it really mean and what do I do?' And then, for instance, yesterday, I suddenly swallowed something the wrong way and so I was coughing and somebody said, 'I was really worried that you were going to have a fit'. I can understand people being worried but they shouldn't be. The amount of stigma there is out of proportion. Really, it's something that I have to change my life to accommodate, but it's not the end of the world to me, and it certainly isn't going to affect other people who know me drastically in any way.

There is a funny side, occasionally. Last year I was having a lot of problems with my speech, in particular, which was worrying me a lot because my job involves a lot of talking on the telephone. I was saying really stupid things, and unfortunately I didn't notice that I was saying them until about five minutes after I'd said them. One day I came in from work and I said, 'Oh thanks, Ian, you've ironed the carpet.' Something made me sort of think, 'That's not quite right,' and then afterwards I thought 'Oh no, I meant to say thanks for *hoovering* the carpet!' But at least I came close.

Emma Wood

Emma Wood, a nurery nurse, has had epilepsy ever since she can remember. In July 1993 she underwent one of the first ever operations to remove the affected area of the temporal lobe of her brain. The operation was possible because of breakthroughs in MRI Scanning (Magnetic Resonance Imaging). Since the operation she has been free of seizures.

There was nothing in particular which used to bring on my seizures. People used to say it was stress, but it wasn't. I was stressed because I had epilepsy. In fact, I never used to think of myself as epileptic because I wasn't told properly that I was epileptic until my teens; but I'd had these feelings ever since I can remember. I especially used to get them when Andy Pandy came out of his box.

I never had tonic-clonic seizures, the jerking and unconscious type. For me it was a feeling: an aura, perhaps. It's a really difficult feeling to explain, like a *déjà-vus*. In my family we used to call them my 'do's'. It was always the same; somebody who was male was in my head, but it wasn't voices, or somebody telling me what was going to happen (although I knew what was going to happen). 'It' would say 'I'm going to get you'; it was that kind of feeling. That was the beginning of the aura. I would know what you were going to do. For example I would know you were going to shake your head, say um, or whatever. It was like playing a tape too quickly; it would get faster and build up to a crescendo. The end was a feeling as if it was saying, 'I've got you again'. Then it would wear down and the first thing I'd say was 'Please, I want a cigarette.' Afterwards, I used to feel exhausted, frightened, with a churning feeling in my stomach the whole time. That would be one fit.

I would carry that feeling of fear with me until the next one. On a bad day I might have about eight fits. On a good day I might have none; but I would still have the feeling, and I'd have one the next day. Occasionally, I might just have one and feel fine. Some days I'd have one, or say only three in a cluster, yet I'd feel like shit for three weeks. They used to come in clusters, and I had to keep a record in my diary. I did this for five years (right up until I had the operation), which was an incredible experience in itself. Each fit was marked with a red dot, so altogether they looked really angry and vicious – every bloody month! At the end of a year I would have had somewhere over two hundred.

This feeling took over the whole concept of how I saw things and felt emotionally towards situations. For example, I'd look outside, I'd look at beautiful things or ugly things, and I'd feel that they weren't right. Obviously everything looked perfectly fine and normal – a chair looked like a chair – but it 'felt' horrible. Everything was emotionally distorted in my mind. I've been told that because it was the right temporal lobe of my brain that was damaged, it was all to do with my emotions. So that has a lot to do with why I felt the fear and anxiety. If it had been on the left it would probably have been a totally different thing. The right side of the brain deals with emotion and logic; when it decides to pack up there is no logic as to why something doesn't look beautiful one day and is amazing another.

I put my family and friends through real shit. I wasn't nice to be with. They all said 'Don't worry, it will pass.' If it happened once a month, for a week, I would have said it was like having a period. You have your period and just think 'Oh shit, I'm going to feel awful for a week.' But it wasn't that sort of feeling. I knew it wasn't for just a week. If it had been, I could have lived with it.

When I was fourteen it got really bad. I stopped eating, and I couldn't sleep. My mother thought I was allergic to something. My stepfather's father (who was a doctor) came and talked to me. I explained how I felt, and he said 'I think you've got *petit-mal*'. I went to see a consultant and had EEGs. Nothing showed up, but they put me on Epilem anyway because it sounded like epilepsy. The seizures stopped for a while; it didn't take them away totally, but it made my life bearable. I could say at that point that I didn't have them any more.

From that moment on, I obviously had epilepsy, but the word wasn't used. It wasn't avoided because it was something to be hushed up, but because I didn't really think I had epilepsy. To me epilepsy was a *grand-mal* (tonic-clonic) seizure; you looked funny and behaved in a very odd way. In my own eyes I wasn't behaving oddly. I just felt odd inside, and so nobody on the outside looking in knew. That's why I managed to hold down a job and carry on a normal life.

Despite that, despite a diagnosis, I felt isolated: Not because nobody cared, but because in the end they got fed up. I'd be saying 'Oh my God I feel awful' and in the end I felt alone because nobody would listen to me. My mother listened, because I think she felt guilty. I'd had a febrile convulsion when I was eight months old, but I wasn't with her, I was with my grandmother. No mother would feel happy if epilepsy was the result of having had the convulsion when she hadn't been there at the time. I really think my mother had her own personal guilt to deal with. She would listen and say she loved me, but nobody or nothing could make my life easier to cope with.

I went to therapy because I was so stressed. One therapist said 'You're angry with your mother', which made me furious. I though 'How dare you say this to me?' She brought five of us up, after my father fucked off. I said 'Don't be so bloody stupid, I'm not angry with my mother. At least she's there. My father's not bloody there.' I said to my mother, 'Apparently I'm angry with you.' She said, 'If you're angry, hit me, for God's sake hit me or do anything, just get it out.' So she was supportive in lots of ways, but I think partly that she felt she had to be; because ultimately she was the one who didn't spot it earlier (until I was fourteen). So with her I think it was guilt. My little brother and sister just thought that I was unhappy and unwell, but weren't quite sure what was going on. My elder sister: I was always jealous of her and wanted to be her, but that might just have been ordinary sibling rivalry.

It got to the point where nobody really believed me; or if they did, they could never understand what I was going through. My brother Matthew, who's a doctor, believed me, but because I carried on with my work he said 'Well, it's not that bad'. I never took a day off because of it, ever. I think it was just a matter of having to keep everything completely in control. If any area of my life was not in control then I'd be frightened; but it wasn't the same sort of fear that I got from a 'do'. If something wasn't a black or white issue, then I'd be scared. Either I liked things or I didn't;

things were never grey or in-between. I was trying so much to be in control, because I knew this monster was going to get me. It would live with me, on my back, and push me down and down. I hated it.

But at least it was familiar. I went to twenty-six schools, and wherever I went this thing came with me. As much as I might have been unhappy at school – I was bullied, but not because of epilepsy – nobody knew. It wasn't that I purposely avoided telling them, it was just that I didn't know it was epilepsy (at least until I was fourteen).

Nor was it because of my epilepsy that I went to so many schools. It was because of my father: he and my mother split up when I was seven. I wasn't thrown out of school, far from it. I was a boring little creep who never did anything wrong. I wish I had. Epilepsy didn't affect my schooling in the usual sense that it affects other people with it. The reason I was bullied wasn't because they were getting a laugh out of me; nobody knew why it happened. It probably did stop me learning to my full potential. My memory wasn't always as good as it could have been. I was knackered after having a fit; I remember falling asleep twice in school after having a fit and having to rest my head on the desk. They always said, 'She could do so much better if she tried harder.' 'She has no confidence' is a phrase that I've taken seriously through my entire life; but at the time I didn't realise how much my epilepsy affected my schooling.

My brother Matthew said, 'You're so normal Emma. You look normal, you behave normally and nobody would know.' I said, 'But I know this isn't normal,' and he admitted 'Only you know how bad you feel.' This was all brought up when the operation was offered. He said, 'Don't do it, don't do it Emma.' I said, 'Well, why not?' He said, 'The risk is just so high compared to what you're doing now. I'd hate to see you come out of the operation paralysed, blind, no memory, no speech or feelings, when before you went in you may have been ill inside, but at least you functioned.' But I only functioned, nothing more. Otherwise I wouldn't have had the operation; I really wouldn't. When I'd had the operation, all my family and friends saw that the problems hadn't just been of my own making. Before, they hadn't known what to think. The situation for them was difficult. Why was it that when I went home I would be fine one minute, then the next I would be miserable, frightened, unhappy, crying, saying I can't go on? Maybe they though I was just being a difficult middle child, maybe they thought I really was ill. I think if it hadn't been for me pushing and pushing for more from the doctors I wouldn't have got anywhere.

I really had to push to get the operation. I even told one doctor to fuck off. I was really angry with him, because all he ever did was make me spit in bottles, checked my blood for drug levels, and asked how I felt. Can you imagine sitting in front of this doctor as he asks you how you feel when you have these seizures? It was so frustrating. Every time I went back to him he would say, 'How have you been?' and I would say fucking awful and he would say, 'How do you feel when you have them?' On this occasion I said, 'I'm not telling you again. Read my notes. If all you want me to do this time is spit in bottles, you can fuck off.' We agreed that it was a clash of personalities, and he said he was going to send me to somebody else. This made me angry at first, because I would have to start all over again with another doctor. I was fed up to the back teeth. Anyway, I wrote and apologized for telling him to fuck off, which I thought was very polite of me, but that I would like to take him up on his offer of sending me to see a new consultant. He referred me to Dr S, probably thinking, 'He'll sort her out.' In fact, I must write to the first doctor and say thank you, because Dr S is brilliant.

He tried every drug on me. One was called Vigabatrin, which has the side-effect of making you anxious. He explained this, and said, 'I just don't think you are the right person to have it, because you're anxious now.' But I said, 'Give it to me, I'll try fucking anything, give it to me. If it stops the fits I'll take it.' He said, 'I don't want you to do anything stupid, to kill yourself. I don't want to tell you about this side-effect, but I know you might feel it.' My brother, Matthew, said I had to give it two weeks, which I did, but it made me feel awful – yet more anxiety to cope with. So after two weeks I stopped. I cried with desperation; I couldn't go on. Dr S tried to cheer me up, saying 'You've got a nice flat, job, friends.' He is a very nice man and I have every admiration for him, as well as for Mr H, the surgeon who eventually did the operation.

Before I had the operation I was taken into hospital for telemetry. This is where electrodes, which send signals to a computer, are attached to your scalp. You are also recorded on video so that they can see what you're doing when you have a fit, as well as the corresponding brain waves. Dr S said 'It won't fit your personality; it's not a happy hospital. I don't want you to think you're going to end up like those people in there. I know you'll hate it. Please don't tell me off.' He probably thought I'd go mad at him ('Don't bloody send me there again!' or something like that). My stepfather phoned; my mother was in America seeing my brother, thank

God. You couldn't leave your daughter there – as far as I was concerned it was like *One Flew Over the Cuckoo's Nest* – but I was normal. One nurse was just like Nurse Crachet in the film. She put the wires on my head, putting more of the glue on me every morning. It wasn't just a gentle little push; she poked me really hard. I know she did it on purpose. 'Medication time, medication time!' It was just like the film. There were video cameras; they could see you but you couldn't see them. I couldn't have a bath wihtout them knowing or being there. I couldn't go to the loo without them, in case I had a fit. I tried to tell them that I knew what I was doing when I had a fit. The most humiliating thing was that they took my medication away. For seventeen, eighteen years I'd taken my own medication, but into the drawer it went. I hated that; they just treated me like everyone else. I'm sure that a lot of the others were perfectly normal people, but being so drugged up they were incapable of taking their own medication, having a bath, or generally looking after themselves. There was no reason to treat me in the same way; I wasn't normal, but nor was I incapable.

It was there that I saw my first epileptic fit; I was epileptic, but I'd never seen a fit. One patient went into a fit as I was going in. It was an incredible scene. Bells were going off, and one nurse said, 'Oh God, it will set them all off now, watch.' And they fitted one after the other; it was just like dominoes. My first up-close experience of a fit was on my first night. It was like an institution, like going back to school where you don't know where to sit on the first day. I asked the nurse, 'Can I sit here?' She said, curtly, 'Just sit anywhere.' But someone said, 'Oi, that's my place, get out.' So again I asked where I should sit, and again the nurse said, 'Just sit down!' This place also turned out to be someone else's, and they said 'Get out of my fucking place!' So I said, 'Right, I don't really want this food,' (it was disgusting). 'I'll go back to my room. Just give me a cup of tea.' Eventually though, I did get it together to eat, and found a space to sit where I thought I was safe; but someone fell on to my table, and bells started going off everywhere because there weren't any nurses in the canteen. A minute later someone else went off, then another. I left because I was quite disturbed by it. There I was with my Rastafarian hair style, wires coming out of my head, and all these people wearing helmets to protect themselves when they fell. These people really were suffering; but I was suffering equally inside.

After I'd spent a week in there, I had the best fit I'd ever had. I pressed the button and said 'Look, look, I've had one! Can I go now?' They said no. 'All you needed was this fit on tape,' I said, 'Can I go now?' 'No you cannot,' they said. 'Stay here at least another day. All night tonight and tomorrow, because you might have another.' I did in fact have another, on waking up.

And so I left. My best friend came to pick me up. She had dropped me there, and hadn't wanted to leave me. When she came in there was an exercise bike which you could cycle on, and sitting on it was a rag doll. It just reminded us of a horror film; it was an image straight out of a nightmare. She threw the doll off. I'm not saying they don't do a good job, because if it hadn't been for the telemetry, they wouldn't have been able to do the operation. It was the way they behaved. For example, one night I was watching myself on the video monitor – not because I'm vain; I don't think I'm attractive – but it had my brain waves superimposed on it, and I was fascinated. If I closed my eyes the waves did something. If I moved my legs they did something else. I had the remote control, but Nurse Crachet came in and snatched it away from me. 'What are you doing,' she said, 'looking at yourself?' She put the remote control high up, as though I wouldn't be able to get up out of my chair and reach it. So I did just that. I was a little rebel. If I'd been at school they'd have written a bad report about me. I got up, got the remote control and flicked it back on.

After the telemetry I had to have an amutol. This is a test which locates where your speech and memory are in your brain. First, they put one half of your brain to sleep, then the other. I didn't realise until I was told afterwards that it's very dodgy. The danger is not that you might die, but that if fluids fail to leave part of your brain you will have a stroke and not come out of it. Anyway, the test was horrible. You're awake, on a thing like a trolley that's not very wide, surrounded by machines; I've never seen so many. Someone is videoing you, you can see pictures of your brain lit up above you, and at the same time you're having an EEG. Also there's a tube inside you from your groin to your neck. They kept saying 'Relax. It will be much easier to get this tube in if you relax.' Relax! Fine, I knew everything was for the best, I want it to happen, but I still couldn't relax. Eventually, though, they got the tube in. Then they said, 'Right, now we're going to inject so many millilitres of fluid into your right side' (which was my bad side). Then they asked me a few simple questions, which I could answer: what my name was, what I did, etc. Then they showed me some pictures, and I had to tell them what each one was and whether I'd seen it before. So they might show me a glass, then another one three cards later, and I would say yes it's a glass and I've seen it before in this particular set. The pictures were those old-fashioned 1970s sort; kind of surreal in a way. Weird things like a purse with a gold clasp, a baby's hairbrush, a cup and saucer. The kind of things which would make me feel worse if I'd had a fit; a boat, but not a nice romantic boat, a really horrible one.

Then they said they were going to inject my good side. I started to worry about how bad I was. What if I couldn't do it? I was really frightened. They said out loud, 'Now I am injecting so many millilitres of fluid, etc.' This was obviously for the video, so they could tell exactly what they'd done, but it was very frightening. They asked exactly the same things again: 'Where do you live?' etc. Then they showed me the pictures as before, and I would say cigarettes, cup and saucer, boat. But when it got to an old-fashioned baby's nappy pin, I couldn't say what it was. I knew I'd seen one of these things before, but I didn't know what it was. I couldn't even say, 'I don't know'. Nothing would come; I felt so frustrated. When I told the therapist afterwards, he asked whether the safety pin had been open or closed. I said it had been closed. He said he thought that because it had been the only thing I hadn't been able to say during the whole test, it meant that I didn't feel safe. So I said he'd better not send all his patients down to have an amutol, because he'd be out of a bloody job. If they couldn't say vagina or penis, they'd be sexually disturbed; that would be the answer, and he'd be out of a job. What if I couldn't say bar of soap? What does that say about cleanliness? I said I didn't think he should pick up on that one. I didn't really think that was the answer to everyone's psychological problems.

So, anyway, they traced where my speech was (in my left side) and where my memory was. Then I had the MRI scan – Magnetic Resources Imaging. If it hadn't been for that I wouldn't have been able to have the operation. It's not like a CAT scan, which most people are familiar with. It shows the inside of your brain from every angle, like an Alice band going through your head. Then all the slices are put together to make up a whole brain inside the computer.

Once I'd had all those I had to have memory and psychological tests, writing and copying. Also tests on my memory and speech. Eventually they said yes, I could have the operation. I was suitable; it was up to me. Somewhere inside I knew I would have it right from the beginning, but to accept verbally was much harder. I went through hours of discussions with family and friends, through the pros and cons, all the risks. The operation and the possibility of dying was very frightening; but if it was going to make me feel better, I wanted it.

Everybody knew about my operation in the buildup to it. In March or April I was told I could have it at Easter. I asked how long it would take to get over it. They said at least two months, and I knew my boss wouldn't give me that time off. So I thought I'd better hold on; I'd have it the first day I broke up in July. I waited an agonizing two and a half months. But it was my decision, my choice. I went around asking everybody 'Would you have it?' They were all hedging their bets. The risks were death, stroke, blindness, loss of memory, loss of speech; I could have been a vegetable. They would say, 'Emma, I don't have the same feelings as you, so I don't know.' People can only relate to their own suffering. So I said to a close friend 'Right, you have this terrible eczema for six months and it won't go away unless you have a major operation. What would you do? Don't tell me now. Go away and think about it.' She came back and said 'I'd do it.' The man that made up my mind to do it was my uncle Michael. He asked 'What's your life like now?' I said, 'Hell'. 'Is the prognosis going to be better or worse if you don't do it?' he asked. I said, 'Worse'. 'If you have the operation, what's the prognosis that it will be a success?' I said, 'Sixty to seventy per cent chance of no more fits, twenty per cent that there might be a reduction in fits, and then a grey bit where I might die.' He looked at me straight and said, 'You've got no choice, have you?' Just like that. When he made me feel like that, it made up my mind.

It wasn't until I was wheeled down to the trolley that my sister realized that maybe I was really ill. Afterwards, I had a lovely letter from my stepfather saying, 'I'm sorry, I feel guilty because I never believed that you were that bad. But seeing you now, after the operation, you're a changed person.' So I think that now there's guilt about how they felt before. My siblings have definitely changed towards me. My sister never wished it on me, or wished me to have more fits; but to see me free and without the devil has been hard to handle. I think to understand how she really feels, you would have to ask her about it. All I can say is that when I got better she didn't like it. She was horrid to me.

I remember the first time I went back home when I was getting better and wasn't having my 'dos'. It was a big family occasion. We were welcoming my brother Matthew and his wife back from America, with their new baby that none of us had met. We were all saying how lovely it was to have them back, and I said, 'Also, I would like to say how happy I am to be able to stand here smiling, not frightened, not having a "do". I'm so happy.' My sister just turned to me, because all of a sudden I was strong. She's got a boyfriend and is happy; and she had just had a baby, so her life had changed dramatically to the same extent that mine had. But from her point of view, mine was freedom and hers was responsibility. Suddenly she looked at me and thought, 'I've never seen her like this. I've never seen my sister say "I'm happy this time and I can stand here with all of you and be really happy to be here."' Having the operation was the best thing I ever did and I felt so good about what I did. It was so obvious to everybody around me that they were looking at this incredibly changed person. I think they would always say or pretend that I was the strongest of the lot. You know, to make you feel better, they'd say 'You're so courageous'. When I got better after the operation, I think my sister thought 'Emma's single and free'. I've always been jealous of her and she's always felt strong because I've been weak; and suddenly I was happy and smiling. This is my interpretation, but she may feel very differently.

Ironically now, after the operation, I'm not completely happy. I'm much happier than I was, much better; but I live in fear. And (although you would have to ask them) I think my family suffer guilt, especially my brother who said 'don't do it'. Being a doctor, he knew more than anyone what a risk I was taking. He phoned my mother a day before the operation and said 'stop her'. She said that it was my choice, and I had to do it. I think they are all feeling bad about it because really no one believed how ill I was until I was on the trolley, or until they saw how the operation had made me happy. It revealed the person they had only seen periodically.

When they put me on the trolley I was screaming hysterically, 'I'm going to die, I'm going to die.' I was even more hysterical when I said goodbye to my mother. They literally had to pull me away from her, and said that she could go down with me. A lovely porter called George held my hand as I was wheeled down to the theatre. Then they put stockings on my legs. I asked what they were for, and they said 'Just in case you get thrombosis.' I thought, 'Well, that's nice to know; you might get thrombosis as well, just an added little bonus to the trip.' Then they said, 'Hop on the trolley'. 'Hop on the trolley?' I said. 'Have you ever hopped on a trolley? Fuck off.' I was saying fuck off to everyone. Then the nurse wheeled me into the lift. You know when you watch *Casualty* and see the lights passing overhead? Well I've lived it. I turned to the nurse who was next to my head, and saw that her name was Susan Brain. I laughed and said, 'I think you ought to change your name. Are you a neurological nurse because of your surname? If you are, you've got a lot to live up to. For God's sake change it to Susan Smith; something dull and boring.'

At the same time that I had the operation, another girl called Sally was having a similar operation; she had scarring on her left temporal lobe. So immediately you think you've got a mate there who's had the same thing. She had the operation two days before me, so when I went into hospital she was sitting up. She had a few fits, but that was fine, as Dr S had explained to me that if you have any fits within the first forty-eight hours they don't class it as a bad reaction or outcome: it's just because your brain has been messed around with; it's rebelling, and the fits might not be anything to do with what they've just done. So I thought that was okay. Two months after the operation I was at home with my mother getting better. Although I was tired, really tired, I was on cloud nine and not at all worried that I was going to have a fit; but Sally phoned me up and told me she'd had one. I went into a big downer. I had to phone up Dr S, and he was brilliant; my aftercare was very good, I have to say. He said, 'You are not Sally, and the fact that she has had a fit doesn't mean you are going to have one. So please relax.' I suppose hearing that helped. Sally wanted to feel that we were in the same boat, but we weren't. My mother was cross that she'd phoned up to tell me she'd had a fit.

Getting better was just like a period before the operation where I might have gone for two weeks without having a fit; but it went on for a bit longer, and longer, and longer . . . it was lovely. I thought that I'd never have that awful feeling again. I was really on a high; it was a feeling of euphoria. I came out of hospital after a week, then I spent six weeks at home with my mother looking after me. She made me eat properly, and made sure I had a sleep every afternoon. She was good company, and really looked after me. When I came back here to my flat on my own, I hit rock bottom; because it felt like everywhere I went the monster was there. Everywhere − in my bedroom, living room. It wasn't there, but the memory of it was, and it felt like I had to go and confront it. I was on my own; no mummy, no doctors, no nurses. All of a sudden I had to get back to normal, and I couldn't; what was normal? I was terrified that I was going to have a fit. Every time I went to a familiar place on my own, it was like facing it again and seeing if it was going to get me there. I had to go to confront it. I'd go to people's flats, people I'd had them with (which is everybody in my life). I thought was it going to get me when I was with Susanna, when I went back to school. It was teasing me. Part of it, when I look back, was me teasing myself. I hate saying this, because it's like tempting fate, but part of me wanted it so that I could say to the doctors: 'See? You failed, didn't you; not even you could get rid of this monster.'

That was the hardest part: to come back and live on my own again. I felt even more alone than when I'd had it with me; at least it was company! There was this gap where it should have been; what was going to take its place? I remember after I'd been here about three weeks I felt even more alone; my flatmate wasn't really around because of work, and I couldn't even phone people up and say I'd had a fit. I could only phone and say 'I'm fine but I'm really lonely.' And there's nothing worse than being lonely when you've got friends. I'd never felt that kind of loneliness before. I really felt as if something had died. At a therapy group I went to, some people talked about the aspect of epilepsy and death. A fit's a bit like death for them, because they lose consciousness and so think they are dying. For me, this was a death; I had to bury it, but I didn't know where. Really it haunted me; it still does, although not to the same extent. The first months when I came back here were the hardest, because I wanted to be happy. I was meant to be thinking that it was great and wonderful, and to be on cloud nine because I was not having my 'dos' any more. I felt bad that I wasn't happy; I felt guilty.

Then one day my sister Rebecca said that I was really miserable. (I didn't need this. I asked myself why I was going to see her. Why didn't I go to see one of my other brothers or sisters?) She said, 'Emma, did you have this operation to be miserable? Because that's what you're doing. If you did have it to be miserable, then go ahead, but I don't think you did.' That's when I realized that I was actually making the anxiety. If I was really strong I'd have to let it go. It couldn't be there, the monster. So I said, 'I'm sorry, you're dead and you're buried. As much as you were horrible I admit that I do miss you; but I'm glad you're dead. I'm sorry you didn't like the way you had to go; you couldn't be drugged down, because you were strong.' To actually kill it, the operation had to be stronger than it, because it was a person. Some people in my group talk about devils and whatnots, but mine is a person; and it wouldn't go until I actually physically cut it out. At that point I was winning. For the first time, I won this battle – I hope.

I say 'hope', because occasionally I still get a strong aura. About three months after the operation, I had an awful feeling that it was coming. It was the first feeling I'd had; but it wasn't the kind of fit I knew. I just freaked, and was shaking. I thought I was having a *grand-mal* fit. I phoned Mummy, she came straight away, and I went back to the hospital again and had an EEG. I was shaking violently, with a really funny feeling down one side, but the EEG was normal. Had I not still been feeling that feeling, had it gone, I would have said, 'I'm sorry you didn't catch it, because it's gone; but luckily I still had the feeling. They said I was having a major panic attack, and was absolutely fine.

I took more time off after the operation than I had done before it. My boss hated me for it, and gave me a hell of a time. The doctor said 'Take it slowly at first and just do mornings.' I did that, and my boss flipped his lid! That incident was the first time that I felt I might be having a fit. The second was when I found out that my father had died (I hadn't seen him since I was ten). All I can say is that if anything was stress related, then these incidents were. They were normal anxiety attacks, but where was the 'do' that went with them? I was looking for it, I created it. When my mother told me that my father was dead, I had a major panic attack. Luckily I was at home. It was awful. I could feel it coming, it was trying to come. Although I had no love for him, I had to try to forgive him. He'd gone, and wasn't there to answer my questions any more (not that he ever would have). So my brain said 'Why, why?'

My clinical pscyhologist, my mother, and Dr S all said 'Your brain looked for an old response. You'd had some really bad news.' Well, what other worse thing could happen to you? It would be to have a fit, and I screamed 'I'm having one, I'm having one.' But if I was to be rational about it, I know that my brain couldn't fire off any more. If you think about how it does it medically, it can't actually go off. The bad connection that used to start the fit is gone; the bad scar that was there isn't there any more. But the feelings that went with it, the auras that warned me, were saying 'I'm coming'. Well, it can still warn me, but he can't get me. He's furious that he can't (I hope) get out any longer.

It is really difficult to separate my emotions from epilepsy. I'm having to rebuild my whole life. I have two birthdays: I'm one year old on 15 July. I can't even walk yet, metaphorically speaking. I really can't. I try, but each time I have an aura, or something makes me fall, and I think I'm not meant to do this without my 'dos'. I also have this secret battle with

God; I really didn't think He was going to make me better, but that He'd punish me even more. He wasn't going to let me die – that would have been too easy. He'd give me a stroke instead. I think that's my secret masochistic aim, although, on the other hand, I've been punished by this thing all my life, so why should everything suddenly be rosy? Nothing has ever gone right for me emotionally. It has certainly stopped me having relationships, because I was cold and frightened, and I knew people could see that in me. I was straight, I was honest, I was strong. I had to be strong, and that put men off. They probably thought, 'I don't know how to handle this person, she needs too much from me.'

Now I can't blame my emotional problems on my 'dos'. I'm not looking for a hook; but I had a hook for twenty-eight years. I could say, 'Well, James has been a shit, work's horrible,' and so on, and then have a 'do'. I would be so focussed on my 'dos' that I never got down to dealing with any real emotional problems; they were just overtaken by my 'dos'. Now I think that somehow I shouldn't have any emotional problems, that my problems were all because of my 'dos'. I'm supposed to be normal, but I'm realizing normal people have emotional problems – fear, anxiety, worries – but I never had all of that with epilepsy. So now I think I make the problem bigger because I'm used to it being huge; I'm not used to having little problems. I remember saying to my mother when I was first getting over it at home, 'If this is what life is like without my 'dos', then life is a piece of fucking piss. What is everybody going on about?' I think that was her happiest day. Right then, life really was a piece of fucking piss. I thought, 'I don't wake up with this feeling any more. I'm not anxious, I'm just fine. Everything looks lovely and it's always going to look like this. Why are all these people saying they're fed up? Life is just a piece of piss without it.' It might well be, in the words of some sentimental song, 'May your life be a rose but without the thorns'. The thorns were the feelings with epilepsy. I really didn't believe that I could sit here without them. I'd have taken heroin, I'd have done anything to take them away, because I was convinced that without those feelings, I was going to be really happy.

Well, it's awful to say, but I'm not happy now. I'm not craving the epilepsy, but I'm not used to life being just normal. It's boring. After my six-month check-up Dr S said to me, 'Well, how are you feeling?' I said, 'I'm happy, really happy, and thanks very much,' but I was telling him what he wanted to hear. He had known me before the operation; he asked if I really meant that I was happy. I told him I was bored. Before the operation eighty per cent of my time had been taken up with me, my own thoughts and feelings. Twenty per cent, if I was lucky, was dealing with life, making plans, thinking ahead. I used to say, 'Gosh, I think I can look forward to next weekend, because I had 'dos' last weekend. And that means that I won't have them this weekend.' I was constantly juggling my life to suit my fits. Suddenly I don't have to, and so now I'm bored.

So what's meant to happen now? I'm meant to be happy. Yes, I could think about changing my career, but in fact I love it more. It's funny, children are like animals; they sense something is wrong with me. I never told the parents, and they never knew, because I could hide it. My boss and my colleagues knew, but they could never tell when I had a fit because I was very good at covering it up. You can say 'I feel awful' in front of friends and family, but not at work. But the children knew when I wasn't well; I'd have fear and anxiety in my face and all over me. When I went back to school in September, after the operation, they were all over me; they had been before, but not to such an extent. Also, after the operation the parents went to the headmistress and said, 'What's happened to Miss Emma? She's changed; she's so happy. Has she got a lover?' (I wish!) Still, to this day, they don't know what's happened to me. One particular parent asked me if I'd had an abortion. I said it had been a long bloody pregnancy! Another asked if I'd had a nervous breakdown.

I didn't tell them, because they'd freak. Well, perhaps they wouldn't freak, but they might say, 'You shouldn't have been working before. But it wouldn't be their place to say that; that was up to my boss, and up to me. I did my job just as well; I wouldn't say better, but I was very focused when I was at work. Work helped me to stop thinking about the devil that was with me. When I was working it was around for one or two minutes a day. When I was busy at school it took me out of my own epileptic world; so in that sense work helped. I was lucky that I didn't have to tell anybody. Actually, if I told them now I'm sure they'd say 'Oh' and probably not even think too much about it. They'd just think, 'No wonder she was unhappy, she was probably just nervous about her operation.' That's why I'm quite prepared to be just Emma Wood, and if they happen to pick up the book they'll work out why she's suddenly got a smile on her face when she didn't for the three years she was teaching before.

So all in all I'm fucking lucky. I'm not saying it's been easy, but it's a lot better. Much, much better.

Before the operation I was very heavily into new catholicism. I really felt desperate, and I wanted to die. I was having major panic attacks, panic that I wouldn't be able to cope any more and would have to go home to live with my mother. My biggest fear was being a 40-year-old woman sitting at home with her 80-year-old mother. My panic attacks were related to that. I felt I was going to lose all control; my head was spinning, and I felt that it was going to explode. It took me over. I was so desperate that in a way the panic attacks even made the fits insignificant. The church has helped. It helped two or three years before my operation, because suddenly I found peace. The people I was working with at the time knew all about my epilepsy, and were really nice and supportive. After I said I wanted to die (although in reality I didn't), a woman I was working with said 'You know, a priest will talk to you at any time.' So I went to see a priest, and while I was in this room, for about half an hour, I didn't have a panic. So I thought there's got to be something in this, and it made me feel better. From that moment, I worked at religion; although I wouldn't say it's the whole story. Now I go back to church and say my prayers and contemplate my new beginning and ask for His help.

I used to be so selfish, and anything that stopped me thinking about me was good. I thought maybe if I did something for other people it would help. I started helping old people by doing teas, because it stopped me thinking about myself. Then I felt selfish because I was doing it for me, not for these poor old women; but they were gaining, so at least that was a positive thing. Then I worked in hospital with people who were dying; I thought at least I'm working with someone who is worse off than I am, but in fact everybody is suffering. I don't know what somebody feels like when they are dying of cancer. I don't know what an old lady feels like when she's lonely because she's a pain to her family and they don't want her. But nor does anybody know how I feel. I felt just as lonely, so maybe I've had something in common with all of them. Catholicism helped me before my operation; and since my operation it has helped me to come to terms with not having epilepsy.

As well, Sally, the clinical psychologist, has been brilliant. I have to stress that the aftercare at the hospital has been great; I couldn't have asked for better. If I needed to speak to them with any problems, they were there for the first two months, and also since I've been home.

I've thrown myself into my job, and tried to keep busy. I'm not living on a cloud any more. I'm just trying to shake off the fear that it might come back. My brother was right, typical bloody doctor. It hasn't been easy. I'm not totally better. I don't think that after sixteen months I'm suddenly going to become cured. I've got twenty-eight years of memories; they don't suddenly go just because I'm not epileptic. I'm not really meant to go out there thinking everything is going to be fine. I've got to cope with other things that I never had to face before. Or maybe I did face them, but only for half an hour, and then they just seemed insignificant. Now they're not so insignificant. Plus there's the fear that I might have a fit.

I've met people who have had this operation, and they've said that if it came back they'd still be grateful to the surgeon for giving them one or two years of fit-free life. Well, I wouldn't. I wouldn't say 'Thank you very much, I really enjoyed those two years,' and be happy with that. I'm sorry, but if I had one now I wouldn't be content. I'd be furious and say, 'Excuse me, get back in there and fucking well get it out, now!'

Roger Symes

Roger Symes has two jobs. He runs his own company which deals with ship finance and international trade. He is also involved with London Disability Arts Forum, an organisation which seeks to promote disabled culture and arts. He is a former Vice Chairman of the British Epilepsy Association but recently resigned as a member of its Council of Management, for reasons which he discusses in his story.

To be pedantic it's very difficult to know when my epilepsy started because my seizures are generalized seizures. I don't have any consciousness while I'm having a seizure and it is possible that I've had seizures for quite a long time before they were actually diagnosed as such – because I was alone and nobody was aware of them.

The first seizure I had that was observed was when I was about twenty-two or twenty-three. I was at home one evening watching television with my parents, and according to them I suddenly fell out of the chair, on to the floor and convulsed in a typical *grand-mal* fit; what's called now a tonic-clonic seizure. That was the first time my epilepsy had been witnessed, and maybe that was the first time that I'd had a seizure, who knows? There was a doctor who lived very close by so my parents called him and he came while I was still coming out of the seizure so it was clearly diagnosed, quite quickly.

I had another seizure about a month later, and quite soon after that I was encouraged to go on medication. I was reluctant to do so at first, but since I've been on medication very seldom have I had seizures. At first I was very hesitant about taking medication because of the perceived side-effects, and also because I didn't have any experience of the seizure. I was aware of watching television and of regaining consciousness afterwards, and a lot of people being concerned for me, but I didn't actually feel that I had experienced the seizure. I didn't have any aura or warning so the seizure wasn't something I was part of; it didn't actually affect me. But I did accept that there was some sort of logic in trying to make sure that it didn't happen again.

When it did happen again about a month later, I decided to take medication, and that's all of twelve years ago now. I've been on the same medication throughout and it's very difficult to know how it affects me because I haven't had any period off. I don't think it affects me particularly, although whenever I feel tired or drowsy I wonder would I not feel that if I wasn't taking the medication? I don't think I have any other possible side-effects; such as swollen gums, or coarsening of facial features which is another supposed side-effect. The drug has basically just become a routine chore for me, and so far I haven't yet considered reducing the medication or coming off it.

Since I've been on medication my history of seizures has been pretty good. I have to qualify that as most of the time I've lived alone and so it may be that I have had seizures that I'm not aware of. In fact, a couple of times I've had instances where, for example, I've woken up and found things lying on the floor, and that's led me to think that I may have had a seizure because otherwise, if I'd knocked something over I'd have just picked it up. Even so, probably I've had several periods when I've gone years without having seizures. The longest period was six years and it may well be that in that time my actual discipline of taking the medication became lax and that is what precipitated the seizures. Perhaps I'd missed a day or even two days' medication. Generally, provided I take the tablets, I'm the ideal patient.

I think all of us feel there's a great overlap in the area between what we feel is epilepsy and what we feel isn't *our* epilepsy. It's something which has come to me more recently. For example, generally, although it's only tested in certain ways, I feel my memory is quite good, compared with other people's. Unfortunately I can't remember anything useful but I can remember thousands of telephone numbers. But occasionally, particularly when I've been seeming to need a lot of sleep and been forever drowsy, I think 'Is this to do with my medication? Or is it very closely linked to how I'm feeling?' If I'm feeling down it's more noticeable than perhaps when I'm feeling up. Then I put it to the back of my mind or the adrenalin keeps me going so I don't appear so tired. So it is very difficult to define what is actually me and what is the result of the medication or the epilepsy.

There may be some psychological component to all this, but I'm not too worried if there is a psychological side. A lot of people are worried about admitting to psychological factors affecting their physical condition. If I look back at when I've had seizures, they often have been during periods when I have been under a particular type of stress; but that said, I don't think I've had enough seizures to be able to draw any real conclusions. There is probably a cumulative effect of not taking the medication, probably not eating well – partly to do with living alone – and a third factor, and if that all comes at the one time, I have the seizure. If somebody said to me, 'You know you needn't have seizures if you organized your life a bit better, or if you learned to handle a certain situation better,' I probably wouldn't do anything about it but I wouldn't dismiss that as a possibility.

I haven't drastically changed my life, though, to accommodate my epilepsy. I think my feeling is quite usual for people who are perceived not to have problems with their epilepsy, and that's a lot to do with how I feel when I have a seizure. Basically, when I have a seizure I don't feel anything; I'm not aware of it. I talk to a lot of other people with epilepsy who have an aura, who have a feeling of partial consciousness, and I'm sure that if I had that type of epilepsy then I probably would feel completely differently. I have no perception or knowledge of the seizure. It's almost as though it's happening in a different room. I think that helps me deal with it.

My first reaction to finding out I had epilepsy is difficult to describe, because now I seriously doubt my own recollection of it. I feel I handled it very well. At the time I had quite a lot of other things going on in my life. I was a navigating officer in the merchant navy. I wanted to leave the navy but I'd found it very difficult to find shore employment while looking around in short periods of leave. I was just due to go back to sea, before Christmas. That meant I would be away for Christmas, and a further six months. I was in love at the time and as I remember it now, the opportunity, because of the epilepsy, that I was not going to have to go back to sea, that I was going to have more time at home, that I was going to have a longer opportunity to look for other employment, all seemed to be more important than the diagnosis.

That recollection is quite different from my parents' recollection of me. They think that I was actually very down. My recollection is that I was busy getting on, trying to make sure that, epilepsy aside, I was going to have a change of career. I think my parents' view was one of concern, as they felt that I was avoiding the issue.

I'm glad that this was going on when I was twenty-two; if it had been going on when I was a lot younger it would have been quite difficult for me to be as positive and as assertive. At the time I handled it as I wanted to, rather than as my parents would have liked me to, and I think I was able to handle it. For example, I put off taking medication until I felt happy to do it rather than taking it straight away. In retrospect that seems sensible to me. Whereas other people around were generally benignly misinformed, I think. They would reassuringly tell you, 'Well, you can live an almost normal life.' It never occured to me that I wouldn't.

However, one of the first things I couldn't do, obviously, was drive, and so I used to have to get the village bus into town to get my CVs copied and that sort of thing. I remember sitting in the bus and somebody with learning difficulties getting on the bus and the two old ladies sitting in front of me whispering to each other, 'He's an epileptic'. I remember thinking 'No, you're wrong! That means I've now got to get out there and tell people.' I believed that it was now my mission to change that view and to show that I wasn't a second-class citizen or whatever. I believed that I was in the 'normal' camp and that I was better than him. I now think that it was an abhorrent thing to have thought but it was very much the avenue that I was directed to.

I did that for about six or eight years: I set out to show that however other people judged me I was on the right side of their line, I was someone who they could identify as being normal. I proved myself. I did get another job but they actually knocked five hundred pounds off my annual salary because I was an epileptic. That didn't defeat me; I was determined to show I was better than everybody else. That carried me through, in that I worked harder than everybody else and I was, in the way that they evaluated me, better than everybody else. I quickly got promotion and was transferred overseas. In that way I was sort of spurred on by the epilepsy but obviously that cost me quite a lot, personally, which I didn't realize at the time. Now I would behave quite differently.

Initially, I had lost my job. That must have caused a deep-seated, but denied resentment. There are a few professions which people with epilepsy aren't allowed to do and one of those is to serve in the merchant navy. So after three months of medical tests I was medically discharged. Again, as I perceived it, it was actually very beneficial. Shipping is a declining industry, and most of my friends at the time were being made redundant, getting small pay-offs. Instead, I got medical severance which was six months' pay, so financially, I did better out of it. I went to work for a Norwegian shipping company in their London office, and got promoted very quickly. After two years they sent me to be manager of their operations in the Middle East. I was there for a couple of years, again working flat out. My girlfriend came over and I pretty well ignored her. These were all the sort of things I was doing to prove myself. After a couple of years I was poached to work in the Netherlands for a few years, and it was after being there that I realized I was quite homesick. When I felt financially strong enough I came back and started my own business here.

The change from this desperate, almost resentful person, keen to prove I was normal and confident, was quite sudden. I came back to this country in 1989. I'd always been a 'joiner' and I'd join masses of clubs and that sort of thing. When I'd originally been diagnosed I joined the British Epilepsy Association. I'd been to local group meetings and due to my sort of drive, I'd quickly become chair of the local group. I was all ready to buy the whole ethos of 'Other people devalue us so we've got to show them that we're all right. It's each man for himself and who gets to the top of the mountain first.' When I came back to England I was ready to resume that role again, got involved with local groups, stood for the national council and was raring to continue the line, along with everyone else who's wrapped up in that sort of ethos.

It was, I think, towards the end of 1989 that one of the local branches had a speaker who was aware of the wider disability movement. She introduced herself as 'I'm sure you're aware of so-and-so': she mentioned some people with epilepsy who were active in the disability movement. I sat there and thought no. None of us knew these people or were aware of what they were doing, so I was curious and wanted to find out more. It was through that curiosity, through meeting Allan Sutherland, through reading his book *Disabled we Stand* that I changed my views. It was like an overnight conversion for me. I read his book which by then was out of print, six or eight years old, and I read every page going 'Yes, yes, yes.' This is how it is!' Straight away it suddenly dawned on me that this whole idea of us as individuals having to prove ourselves by other people's standards was wrong, and that as long as we kept doing that we would never achieve anything collectively. If we actually wanted collectively to achieve some of the aims which we support and which we as an organization say we support, then actually doing it on an individual basis was absolutely ridiculous. It was a real revelation to me.

Then I quickly tried to glean as much information as possible, and from that met a lot of other people and realized that there is no such thing as normal. I had been convinced that epileptics are normal. 'If you can't consider us as normal, well at least consider us as normal ninety-nine per cent of the time, and therefore it's not right to label us, particularly as disabled or handicapped or anything. All those labels carry an element of pity and I don't want that, thanks.' That's certainly the line that I was advocating before. To realize that it was completely wrong and that a lot of people who had other impairments, such as blindness, deafness, use of wheel-chairs or whatever, are concerned about exactly the same issues as me was very powerful. The only difference was that often people with epilepsy could control the time of disclosure about their condition; not always, but often could. That has maybe contributed to leading us away from a lot of people who are really our allies.

I think the ethos that I subscribe to now is very much based on doing away with the preconception that there are 'them and us', that there's people that are like us, there's people we accept and that there's people who we don't, and we go through life sorting people into those two categories; and the category which generally falls on the wrong side of a lot of people's line is disabled people. Now I think that disabled people should get together and work at rubbing out that line. That's very much what the civil rights movement is all about and it's what I identify very much with. The alternative is to work individually, with the idea that if I'm nice to you, you'll let me creep across to the right side of your line. That may work temporarily for a few people, but it's not something that I would be proud of now.

While this all may sound like a political awakening and not a lot else, it did have an effect on my emotions; psychologically it made me feel better. It gave me permission to think that a lot of the things I had denied myself or perhaps viewed in myself as being signs of weakness, were okay. Before, I hadn't allowed myself to feel those things because that was negative and I had to get on and be positive and act. But now I could look at a lot of things in a different way. For example, I could view other people's unreasonable behaviour and admit that it was all right to feel angry, hurt, cross, frustrated or just disappointed by their behaviour regarding epilepsy. It doesn't mean that if someone else's behaviour is unacceptable, hurtful, or whatever that you have to take it and drive yourself alone to overcome it. You can just acknowledge it for what it is.

I'm also more confident and assertive about talking about my condition. I'm still not as good as I would like to be. I think I'm getting better at it, but I still don't feel comfortable in how I do it because I'm still unable, I think, to announce it or convey it in a way that I'm happy with. Unfortunately, whenever I talk about my condition to non-disabled people, there is always a hint of apology in my voice, and however much I practise it and however much I try and rephrase it, there is still a little hint of self-deprecation in my voice. People who want facts and information, I think that's fine, and I'm quite good at putting that across and I acknowledge their reasons for wanting to know, but it's when the issue clouds between factual information and other information about me as an individual or how my medical condition affects my life, that I find harder.

However, I do find it easier now, to be open about my epilepsy. Many people are so keen to be seen as normal, that they can't be open about it. I don't criticize people in that situation, partly because certainly in the past, that was the way I followed and I perceived it to be the only way. It wasn't that I had viewed a variety of options, and chosen that way, and that was how I was going to handle it. It seemed the only way at the time to get on, was to conceal where possible. I think that most people who do keep their epilepsy very much concealed feel that there are very valid reasons for it, and often they are reasons which a lot of other people would identify with. I hope that as the wider disability movement comes forward we will pick up some of those people and take them along, that they'll want to join us. At the moment, they've got a lot of history, fear and pressure from those around them, and from everybody who's advised them that being open isn't the best way, so they're not going to shake that off overnight but I hope that they will join us. Obviously I hope we'll get a snowball effect that as the movement grows bigger then more people will join it, but I can't offer any quick-fix solutions to people, particularly for people who've had parental pressure, family pressure, cultural pressure, pressure at work, that sort of thing. The idea that I should say to them, 'There is nothing to be ashamed about with your epilepsy,' is incredibly naïve.

However, from my new perspective, I'm really disappointed by the approach to dealing with epilepsy by the major charities. One of the first things I did when I found out about the wider disability movement, was to attend a conference called Cap in Hand which was organized by disabled people. A lot of the people with various impairments there were very angry about the way their charities represented them. I remember thinking at that time, that at the British Epilepsy Association, we don't have a lot of these problems, we've got a lot of people with epilepsy involved in the organization, we don't have that old ethos of actually running a care home or a colony or whatever; and I felt very encouraged. Now, five years later, when I see how so many of the other charities have moved on, have recognized user-empowerment and the importance of user-involvement in decision making, I'm very frustrated that the BEA, which I perceived as having a lead, has stayed still and while many other organizations have moved ahead.

There are, I think, something like twenty epilepsy charities in this country, and at least half of those are based around residential institutions. All the epilepsy organizations get together and have twice-yearly meetings and that sort of thing. Now I would like to actually see some of the organizations, if they really are supporting people with epilepsy, come away from that and say 'Look, residential care for people with epilepsy is no longer appropriate. There are options which are open to people now which mean that the idea of containment, which is what the original colonies were set up for a hundred years ago, is no longer appropriate.' Unfortunately too many of the community organizations are still funnelling people towards the residential institutions. So rather than trying to break down walls, walls which are very shaky and crumbling, the community organizations are working to patch them up. It means that, for example, parents of young children with epilepsy who want advice are quite often going to be funnelled towards a residential institution in another part of the country.

I know that everyone with epilepsy is different and you can't make sweeping judgements that suit one and all. That's unfortunately the argument that is always thrown against us, you know, 'My Johnny isn't like you. It's very easy for you to say these things.' As an example, take a five year old girl having two or three *grand-mal* fits a day. It's a difficult physical condition for the parents to deal with, and they may reluctantly feel that there's no alternative to residential care for her. They're saying 'Our daughter can't look after herself. She can't go to the shops on her own,' or the like. Well, I know a lot of people who have very serious impairments, who require assistance all the time and those people have helpers with them who can provide that assistance but they don't provide control. I know that's true for children as well, because there are examples of good practice in this country. Amazingly what surprised me was that quite a lot of the children in the residential establishments have a full-time support worker working with them. If the child has a full-time support worker with them in remote Cheshire, why can't they have a full time support worker with them in their inner London borough? There's absolutely no reason. The parents don't perceive that, or they're not told that that is an option. They're told the option is send your child to Cheshire and your child will be looked after. They're not told that there is another option which may not be as readily available but can be fought for and is your right to fight for, which will actually enable you to have a proper parent-child relationship, not push you into forty years of dependency – forty years of full time care – but will actually enable both you and your child to develop in the way a family should do.

There are parents' support organizations across the full range of disabilities. This isn't something you need to think about just because your child has epilepsy. It might be that your child has cerebral palsy or any other impairment, and there are very strong parents' organizations fighting for better services at home. Fortunately, of course, many local authorities also realize that this is an option they should be providing and they are actually now refusing to finance sending a child half-way across the country to a boarding establishment when more appropriate services could be provided for the child in their locality. The trouble is that single solutions are often presented to parents by people who wish to maintain these establishments, which employ a massive number of people and have huge turnovers. They say 'This is the option: if you care for your child you will send it away.' If that is presented as the only option, it is very difficult for a parent who isn't aware of other options and feels at the moment they can't cope and that the child is wearing them down; in fact the parent has no knowledge. Self-advocacy starts with knowing the options that are available. If you don't know the options, you can't make an informed decision.

However, to be fair, I suppose I ought to qualify what I am saying by admitting that perhaps I'm the wrong person to judge these organizations. They weren't set up by people with epilepsy, they were set up to meet other people's needs, the needs of parents and the needs of professionals who worked with epilepsy. Perhaps I should accept that, and perhaps other people like myself with epilepsy should not actually try to go into these organizations and change them round to our way of thinking. Perhaps we should be setting up our own organizations. Organizations such as the British Epilepsy Association and the National Society for Epilepsy come from, first of all, a very medical perspective: that is, somebody is ill and you want to make them better; the treatment normally involves medication, and therefore success is measured in that sort of way.

The whole ethos is based on the doctor-patient relationship, very rarely one of equals; certainly it wasn't decades ago. The charities are still burdened with that relationship of expert, professional expert, and ignorant patient. When you take that into a charity management set-up, it doesn't change. You still have a situation where people may be equal around the table in the way they can vote, or in their potential input into decisions but the image remains of one person as being the expert and the other person as being the passive recipient of expert advice.

A major problem that doctors will tell you about, or one of the main problems, is what they call non-compliance, which is that people don't take their tablets when they should; they don't comply with the medical advice they've been given because the patients don't perceive the need to comply. People take most medication when they're ill, and when they're not ill, they stop taking the medication. Epilepsy medication is all about taking it when you are well in order to stay well and if that isn't explained or people don't understand it, then if they haven't had seizures for a while, they stop taking the medication. The main thrust of the doctors argument is that patients don't carry out the instructions given to them by doctors. I can understand that from a medical view it must be very frustrating.

Unfortunately, that very simple relationship extends across the whole field of epilepsy care. Doctors have years of training, doctors study, doctors see a hundred patients or even a thousand patients with epilepsy. Doctors go to all the medical conferences so therefore they must be the experts, because their exposure to the condition, they would argue, is much wider than any individual's. They would also argue – probably because when they normally see patients across the consulting table they are there to talk about the individual's condition – that individuals are obsessed by their own condition.

They think I can't make a case for what I think would be a good service for people with epilepsy, I can only make a case about what I consider would be good for me because that's how our relationship normally is; we're talking about my condition. It is a very disempowering situation. I think it is so powerful that I'm conscious of how it affects me. I often did things looking for appreciation or praise from a medical expert. I hope I don't do it so much now, but when I look back at my time actively with BEA, I think there were a lot of things I did because I wanted a pat on the head; not because they actually were what I wanted to do but because I wanted to be perceived as someone who was doing what someone else thought was good for me.

It comes down to being responsible for your own condition and being empowered enough to analyse the risk in one's own life. Dealing with epilepsy is kind of risk analysis in a way. I used to feel that as a group of people we're not actually able to do that, or capable of doing that; that the doctors felt we would make the wrong, or too risky decisions about our own situations. For example, I was with somebody at a big epilepsy conference a couple of years ago. We were at a party and I remember one of the people there saying to me, 'If I don't want to have a fit tomorrow morning, I should go home now, but I'm having a good time, I'm going to carry on and I know that I will have a seizure in the morning. After weighing it up I would rather go through that.' I think that's a perfectly reasonable decision, I think it's great, that somebody has taken that decision. What frustrates me so much more is when I meet other people, for example at group meetings, and we say afterwards, 'Who's coming round to the pub?' and some people say, 'Well, my doctor has told me not to drink'. It is so ingrained, that the idea that they couldn't even go into a pub and have a coke or a lemonade or something has escaped them. They believe that the doctor's rule is to be obeyed to the letter, and it is all so overwhelming that sometimes it happens, and we're not aware of it.

To be kind to the doctors or the medical profession, this unbalanced relationship also places a tremendous burden on them and I know a few of them are not happy with that burden. They would much rather have an equal relationship with their patients and they would much rather that the responsibilities were more evenly shared. But most doctors have gone through a mill which produces them at the other end to believe that a patient isn't going to do what the doctor says, say, unless they respect the doctor, and unless they do what they're told the patient isn't going to get better. So if the patient starts thinking, 'Well, mmm, maybe this isn't right,' then that's a problem. That's why, unfortunately, in groups you see people who say, 'Well, you know, I take these tablets but I know they're not doing me any good.' And you say, 'How long have you been taking them?' and they've been taking them for months. 'Well, are they better than your last tablets?' 'No, they've made me worse but the doctor told me to take them.'

There's a need to challenge, or at least discuss medical opinion, but most of us feel very reluctant to do it, and that carries on even when we move out of medical surroundings. In a charity situation, sitting round the committee table, if the doctor present says, 'This month's donations are not very healthy because of x, y and z,' we, the epileptics, all tend to think he's the expert, he knows. But he's no more an expert on how donations have been received or how money has been spent than anybody else. That at least is my experience of going to numerous committee meetings.

There is, of course, the need for more information on the front line, at the time of diagnosis, and more support on initial contact with the medical profession, both for the patient and the parents. But there's a danger in saying that: it's more complex than that. It's a bit like saying, 'Do you think we need nurses in hospitals?' Yes, of course, nobody's going to say you don't, but then you have to ask, 'How many do we need and what exactly should they be doing, or what are the priorities?' The question of initial support is very complex. Certainly the traditional role of the voluntary organizations, or at least they way would see their role, is to provide individual support at that time. Later on, they see their role as quasi-medical support.

For example, you go in to see your doctor, the doctor says you've got epilepsy, take these tablets for the rest of your life, next please. You go out in a daze and you look at the waiting room notice board as you leave, see the British Epilepsy Association poster or whatever. You ring them and they give you the facts that perhaps you should have been told by the doctor. They send you a leaflet, you become a member, you send them ten quid at Christmas, and they provide an extra level of information you need. My personal assessment of that service is that it works for some people. If people know about the service and if they ask the right questions they will get the right answers. I can't say anything more than that, really. It doesn't work as well as it could do, often because people don't know the questions to ask and often the questions they do ask are not really the ones they want answered.

What I dislike about the quasi-medical aspect of the charities is that the charities start from the basis that there is a problem, the problem is set in stone, and how do we mitigate its effect? I take the view that there are lots of problems and how do we remove them?

Let's stick with the example of somebody who's newly diagnosed. He goes to his doctor and the doctor says 'You have epilepsy and the solution is to take these tablets. Ring me up every two months for a repeat prescription or whatever? Now the specific problem there is that the person has had inadequate treatment. He needs to know more information, so the charity or the BEA solution is to provide him with the information he needs. That helps at one level. It works in that instance but it doesn't have any other effect on your life and doesn't influence anybody else. My solution might be that you go and see the doctor, you then contact somebody else who says, 'Well, actually, what you have received from your doctor isn't good enough. You have a right to better treatment than this.' You would have a support mechanism so that you could get advice, advocacy skills, training or whatever. So then in a year's time, when your seizures start changing or something goes wrong, you know what to do the next time you go and see the doctor. You actually say what you want, you change that doctor-patient relationship, talk it through, get your point across, voice you fears. This is better than a situation where you go and see the doctor who says, well, 'We'll up your dosage, and see how that goes for a few months.' You go out totally demoralized, and possibly you ring up BEA. BEA will say 'Stick with it' or something, or perhaps they'll say 'That is rather high, but see how it goes.' In that approach, nothing has changed, whereas I believe that people need to get the skills to get rid of the problem with the doctor for good.

Within the charities there is what strikes me as the germ of a strong, powerful force. That is the local meetings. There, lots of people with epilepsy share experiences in an informal way. Some of them are very good at dealing with the medical profession, some are having a hell of a problem getting their head round advocacy. But it's happening despite the nature of the national organisation: those people could get together anyway and have that meeting. You don't need a national head office, you don't need all those other things to benefit from local contact and shared experience.

In fact, a national head office can be very counter-productive because it distracts you away from the real need. You get together locally, you identify what your real need is. For example, you might say, 'the doctors here are crap, they know nothing whatever about epilepsy; we can't communicate with them properly. What do we need? We need to be able to address those problems; we need to get different sorts of help, learn skills which we don't have in order that we can address that problem. We need to campaign for our own rights.' Instead, having the head office distracts you because you're told, 'Head office is having a national campaign for X, Y and Z.' Or national head office is where you go for the information rather than choosing information from the sources. Straight away it's disempowering and it's focusing your direction away from your needs to a more general esoteric need.

The problem is that if you're running an organization like that, there is a head office syndrome where you feel the need to control: 'What are they talking about in Ealing? What are they doing this month in Scotland? We need to focus *them*, we need to tell them what to do, they're using our name. For example, one group might say that Dr Bloggs is useless, but he is on our medical advisory panel, so we want to make sure they don't step over the mark.' There's that need to focus and control. The organization can also be like an engine that needs coal, i.e. donations shovelled into it all the time. It's a distraction. They say, 'The money you raise, shovel it up to us and we will put it into X, Y and Z.' That's what has happened with the large charity organizations – the head office no longer supports the local needs.

Admittedly, you can't do away with some sort of national co-ordination, but not in the way it is now. It would make sense, for example, if there were a lot of local groups, to have a national resource which could service those groups. Unfortunately – and I'm not just talking about BEA, I'm talking about a lot of organizations – when that relationship changes and becomes one of local serfs and national masters, then sooner or later people move away from it because it isn't giving them what they need. They split off. The trouble is that they often think they need another national organization so it's often as if they go out of the frying pan into the fire. I have to say that although I think BEA has faults, it's one of the better epilepsy organizations. There are other organizations who are much more rooted in the ethos of the past.

I've talked about the medical profession and to sum up I think there is a strong tendency within it to resist change, a force against the self-help ethos for people with epilepsy. It's subtly, institutionally, against the goal of user empowerment. The other equally effective force against change is some parents, particularly those whose children grew up some time ago, who are now of adult age. The parents did what they were told by the medical profession when their children were diagnosed and that's what they've always tried to do. They've always tried to do their best for Johnny, they've tried to always mitigate against other people's perception of his condition; they wanted to feel they had a normal child. I'm aware of this all the time. The way it comes across most obviously is with parents whose children, for whatever reason, have not left home so that the relationship has remained of a dominant parent and a young child, even though chronologically that might not be correct. That relationship includes a need by the parent to speak for that person, to dictate how that person should live their life. It might have been appropriate when that child was primary-school age but is no longer appropriate when that 'child' is thirty or forty.

That attitude then carries on into a committee relationship, for example, because they are used to controlling other people's lives. That's what happens in their own home; they say what should be done and it is done. They then come into a committee situation and see someone the equivalent of their child sitting across the table and if that person with epilepsy disagrees with them about something, it is difficult for the parent to accept. So there's two equally important groups against change. And when someone like me suggests change, or starting to change, their instant reaction is, 'Oh my God! You don't know. You're not capable of making that decision.' Your decision, they feel, is not made in the appropriate way. It is only appropriate for someone else to make decisions for you. For example, if my decision were to stop taking drugs and to see what happens, I'd be doing that out of resentment about not being normal, because I haven't come to terms with my condition. There's a lot of things, but that's a typical one. There's also of course the fear that actually I might be fine if I stopped taking drugs, and therefore what does that say about everything else they are supporting and going on for? The chance of you succeeding is obviously very, very threatening, because maybe that means there's lots of people like you who shouldn't be taking their tablets, and if they're always telling everybody it's important to do that, where does that leave them? That's a major problem but overriding that is their concern about you taking a decision which is, in their view, not your decision to take. That's why I feel my allies are more likely to be people who've shared my experience even though they may have different impairments, than parents or the medical profession.

I see quite a difference between organizations *of* people with disabilities, *of* people with epilepsy, and organizations *for* people with epilepsy or other impairments. I don't think it is possible for an organization to do both, to be *for* and *of*. You cannot meet the needs of the sort of parents I have talked about, the medical profession *and* people with epilepsy all at the same time.

No one wants to be denied the full range of possibilities in our society. My solution is that we should throw our lot in with the rest of the disabled population and fight discrimination. I don't go along with the approach that if we get rid of the condition, we'll be normal. The fact is we do have epilepsy now, and if we want to have equal opportunities in education, work, housing and so forth, we need to join forces with other people who also want these things and aren't getting them because they are disabled by society.

I am defining disability in terms of social character, ie, those people who are discriminated against on the basis of a physical difference or a mental difference. That would include epilepsy, people with severe dermatitis; people who are diabetic could join the disability movement. People who have lost jobs because they don't look right, they don't sound right. It seems to me self evident that if people don't get jobs because they are black, then the thing to do is fight that, not make yourself less black. It's the same type of problem.

If we talk about this mythical Johnny again and look at the problems that Johnny is likely to face in his life, it may be easy to say that these problems are caused by his epilepsy, but actually those problems result from how other people interact with him. Their view of him will have nothing to do with the medical definition of epilepsy. People will not interact with him from an informed view of knowing about his condition. We already know that every person with epilepsy has a different type of condition. Epilepsy takes different forms, so people are not going to say, 'Ah, his epilepsy means that he has tonic-clonic seizures, that he has myclonic jerks,' etc. They're going to react to the word and they're going to link it with other words which have negative connotations, so in that way it's nothing to do with the medical condition. That's why I try to say to people with epilepsy who think it is very much down to their medical condition, 'Look at it purely medically. How many seizures do you have? If you only had half as many seizures would you be treated differently? You wouldn't be treated differently when you see on a form "Have you any pre-existing medical conditions?" and you write epilepsy; you probably wouldn't be treated any differently in most other spheres as well. It has absolutely nothing to do with the actual manifestations of your condition.'

Somebody with epilepsy does not have civil rights, unfortunately. At the moment, people with epilepsy are offered – by parents and doctors, and by their own sense of what having a disability means – a notion of you've got to be better, you've got to try harder, you've got to gain more qualifications, you've got to over-compensate. Those are the options available to people on a purely individual basis. But on the collective level, I think there needs to be legislation which means that epilepsy does not become a factor in job selection or how you are treated at work, other than how it would affect you ability to do that job. Basically that means if somebody rejects you on the basis of a word on an application form you would have the right to have it challenged. Employers would then realize that it was invalid, that they had no right to do it. I'm not saying that this will change things overnight, but at the moment there is nothing to stop somebody discriminating and feeling that they have done the correct thing. I think it would mean a lot for people with epilepsy to feel that, if they have been discriminated against – and I'm not saying that every time somebody feels they've been discriminated against they have been – but they would have a mechanism to challenge it. They would actually know that there is a means of redress. People with epilepsy would be able to feel that this is not something about which our conventional wisdom says, 'Well, that's life, you will get discriminated against.' Our wisdom will be 'That's wrong, we want to change it.'

I recognise that there are great psychological problems for many people with epilepsy in joining the wider movement of disabled people. This is because of the nature of the condition, in that it is a hidden disability, or it's intermittent, and so there are extra pressures on people with epilepsy. For example, personally, I haven't quite found the form of words I feel comfortable with when I do disclose the fact I have epilepsy. Normally, however I do disclose it, it's followed by a little nervous laugh, a little bit of self-deprecation or justification or something. That sort of thing puts pressure on you because it's your presentation that lets you down. You went for the interview, you didn't get the job: well, that's because you didn't put it across in a positive enough way. Did you stress the benefits? So it's seen very much as being down to you, to how you tell someone you have epilepsy. That actually what has happened is that you have handled that situation badly. Again, it was down to you as an individual and you failed that test. It's no surprise then that people hide their condition. 'If I can control the situations where I experience discrimination by choosing when and where not to disclose,' the individual's logic goes, therefore, 'I don't actually need to align myself with the disability movement. For instance, I know I only have seizures when I wake up in the morning, so I've never told anybody at work. I know if I did tell them at work there'd be problems, but I've no need to etc.' I think it is quite difficult to tell people with epilepsy, who for a long time have used that option of non-disclosure to protect themselves, that it's actually okay to say something. The good thing to say now, is that I know more people with epilepsy probably outside the charity circle than I do inside it. So there are a lot of us out there already, it's not as bad as you might think. It quite amused me that in the charity world I was seen as a radical with brand new ideas. In fact, the ideas have been around for ten, fifteen years and I'm not the only one who thinks like this. The difference is I was the only epileptic who, instead of disappearing to where I was welcome, spent a long time where I wasn't welcome, trying to change things.

Ironically, it can be a bit disarming to be in the wider disability movement and feel a bit out of place at first. My perceptions of disability had, I think, conditioned me to think when I first became involved with the movement, not so much that I was inadequate in that I wasn't severely impaired enough, but that other people would judge me. One of the nicest things, one of the most positive things about the disability movement is that I have never been judged in that way. There's been no hierarchy and no judgement in any way.

Sue Backham

Sue Backham is not working and has been on invalidity benefit for a long time because of ill health and a head injury. To keep occupied, she structures her week as if she has a part-time job. She does cabinet making, ceramics and yoga. At present her diagnosis of epilepsy is yet to be confirmed. She regulary has fits and is not on any medication.

I went to a medical rehabilitation centre and I saw the consultant in rehab medicine who had trained as a neurologist. She said my symptoms were consistent with temporal-lobe epilepsy. She suggested I see a neurologist, whom I haven't seen yet because my GP is being quite obstructive, for some reason. That may be because I have had another serious medical problem for which I didn't want surgery and they've been quite unhelpful since then.

My symptoms are like this. When I have, what seems to be a seizure if I was eating I wouldn't be able to chew and I would not be able to swallow and start choking. The colour green would stand out projected. I would have to wear dark glasses if it was sunny, avoid looking at railings or reflections on water and I would get involuntary tears or tears welling up. I would walk with a funny step like a dance, and be very aware of strong overpowering smells. I couldn't grasp the meaning of things said to me, I couldn't write or speak properly, I'd get numbers back to front. I would get a feeling like electricity in my head, and see lights in my head.

Burning myself would also be a big problem. Once I put my bare hands in the oven and picked up a hot casserole. I would know I'd been burnt afterwards but at the time it never occured to me that I might have been. My fingers are not badly scarred now but that was the most distressing thing for me so far. It's like a loss of awareness. Even when getting in a hot bath, I could feel it was burning me but I couldn't stop myself, in the same way as I put my hands into the cooker. My sister, who saw me do it, said I was just automatic, like a robot.

I also described to the doctor that my whole left side would go quite dead, sometimes but not necessarily with a migraine. That's what bothered me most. If I was walking, sometimes the left side would go. I'd be aware of it and I'd be aware that I'd be walking oddly. It's like the leg had got shorter, because I was missing my footing. Years ago I would tell the doctor that I had the same problem while driving. I used to get it in the car and keep driving and driving and end up on the North Circular not knowing where I was, or I'd even end up in somebody's front drive. (I stopped driving voluntarily because I didn't feel safe and it was bothering me. It was a big problem).

I think I've had this all my life because I remember, when I was a child, places where I had these strange sensations. I remember them because they might have been frightening experiences or bad ones where I'd got lost or was alone. I would always get very frightened. It happened today in fact. Sometimes I would see a man who wasn't there in a black cloak and a black hat. I used to get very bothered back then and think I was going off my head. I've joined a group of people with epilepsy, and finding they have had similar experiences has stopped me worrying so much. Talking to the other people and hearing they have similar things is good. Somebody else in the group experiences the 'getting lost' problem.

One type of incident that's happened to me a lot is that I've gone on the Tube, known I should get out at a certain station and then I've lost a few stops. I've lost time and I'll come out and I'll be very confused, not know where I am and have to ask a policeman. It's as if I'm drunk and I just don't know where I am. That used to terrify me and I thought it was low blood sugar. Everybody kept saying 'you've got to eat regularly,' but I was. When it was happening after meals, knowing therefore I wasn't hungry, I got really bothered. I had one yesterday after a meal. I was walking around in a world of my own. I'd called a cab and it came at six, but by the time I got down it was twelve minutes past. I'd been wandering about, unaware. I keep doing that: doing repetitive things such as putting my head band on, fiddling with my bag, or cleaning my glasses. When I'm doing these repetitive actions I'm not completely out of it because I know I'm doing them but I can't stop and that's what I hate the most. I hate anybody witnessing it.

So I trusted what the consultant at the medical rehab centre had to say. She said a lot of migrainers have a tendency towards temperal-lobe epilepsy, and she asked me about *déjà vu*. I got that yesterday; a lot of women say it's tied into their menstrual cycle, and it is with me. Yesterday I was in a cab and I knew the driver wasn't going to have any change and when we got there she said 'I don't have any change'. I knew she would say that. When I was in the cab everything was flying around because the street lights passing outside affect me. Another frequent thing with me is knowing what people are going to say. I used to do that a lot with people and they'd say, 'How did you know?' I just used to think it was being psychic. Psychic things seem to be controlled, but the experience I have in this state is not controlled, and its the feeling of being out of control that I hate. An instance that I can give is when my niece was at my place. She was playing with the little girl from next door who was rattling on the letter box for ages. That repetitive sound set me off. I felt totally out of control and just kept going round and round and feeling odd in my head. It's a bit like being under attack. It's like maybe being in a war and being shelled, or swimming in air, a drunk feeling like when you're really drunk and you're staggering about. I've fallen a lot and I've often hit my head where I've missed my footing. I trip up the stairs and hit my head. It used to happen in brightly lit shops; I didn't know what it was and that the lights triggered it.

I had no idea this was all consistent with epilepsy. I had a preconceived idea that most people have, that an epileptic person foams at the mouth and crashes to the ground. I know it sounds awful but I'm being honest because I thought that was what happened. I thought people collapsed and you had to put their heads to the side and put a pillow under the head and keep them comfortable. I've been in the street and I saw it happen to somebody, and a little voice inside me said 'That's an epileptic, you have to keep them warm and turn their head to the side.' Everybody was saying 'She's diabetic' but this little voice kept saying 'No, she's epileptic, she's not diabetic'. Somebody from the pub was trying to force a glass of water in the woman's mouth. I stopped a police car, and said to the policeman 'Have you got a blanket? Get one out the boot and wrap her up.' We looked in her pocket and she carried a card saying she was epileptic. I was right, but I felt very emotional when I saw these people, fussing around her. I felt very choked.

When I was little, I can recall an instance when I went on a picnic and I was told to hold the beach ball. I don't know where I got the pin from but I remember just stabbing it all over. Of course I got a clout because the ball went down, but I kept saying it wasn't me doing it. I remember being very upset that they didn't understand that it wasn't me, it wasn't naughtiness. I wasn't a naughty child. I suppose having it as a child, and not being told any differently, you would just think that that's the way you are. My mum always said that I was very eager as a child but I'd just not 'be there' sometimes. She'd say the same about my sister. She used to call it something on the lines of brain dead, but it wasn't cruel. 'Not quite there, in a world of your own and wouldn't respond.' My mum said that I'd be talking and talking and I'd be off somewhere, just not there at all.

Being told that I have epilepsy has released the whole of my life that's gone before. It's sort of like a healing thing. I know homeopathy has helped, as well as woodwork and pottery, but it's like a cloud's lifted because there are other people like me. Now I can just get on with my life because I can laugh and think well, you've got it, and these other people have got it. It was the not knowing, it was being told that it was nothing, being dismissed all the time that I found very depressing. I would keep being dismissed.

The worst thing for me was that it could happen to me while I'm in the doctor's, so then I couldn't assert myself. I'd be sitting there, sort of staring into space or my speech would get all jumbled. I'd get stressed out about going to the doctor's and sometimes not get there on time, or not get there at all. Then they would throw a lot a lot of stuff at me like, 'You didn't turn up for your appointment' and then I'd say that I'd written them a letter telling them I have these funny turns. I've got loads of letters saying I can't come, because when I get half-way there I get lost or have these funny symptoms and I don't know what they are. And they kept saying make another appointment and I kept saying I do come, but when I get here, because of these attacks I can't find the floor or the clinic! So after getting lost again and again and ending up on Highgate Hill or Waterloo Park or something, I was just getting so depressed and upset by it all, I thought, 'What the hell is wrong with me?' I was then doubting myself. I was thinking 'Is it just stress?' because one doctor said it was stress.

Nobody was willing to refer me to a neurologist or anybody who could deal with it. I don't know if that was because they were familiar with neurological symptoms. I certainly don't think these people were qualified enough. One day I was at Wood Green and I walked like a robot from there to my doctor's surgery. It was a sunny day and I was walking past railings and I must have been having a fit that lasted all the way. I think it was about three miles but I just walked, and when I got there I was really confused and late. They said 'You'll have to come back another day,' and this is what happens all the time. I just wanted somebody to see me while it was happening, but they sent me away.

I think I'd like to see an independent neurologist, maybe somebody recommended, somebody who really knows what they're talking about, who isn't going to dismiss me and is going to listen to what I've got to say. When I had these fit-like feelings all day long, all the time, I felt drunk all the time, so I couldn't get much done. But I persevered. I just thought that there must be an answer and I'm very determined, I'm very strong willed fortunately. I thought, 'Well, what I'll do is be methodical. I'll take a bit at a time and try and solve it.' For me, it's the last piece of the jigsaw being diagnosed, albeit unconfirmed. I feel quite excited about the idea of it being epilepsy. It explains so much. I actually feel quite positive about it.

I had relatives who had similar feelings. A grandfather was labelled mad or had funny turns and he ended up in a mental hospital where he died. So did an uncle. Mum said he used to turn up at the door, all vacant. I said this sounds to me as if it's definitely in the family but no one will admit to it; they don't want to discuss it at all. I'm not ashamed of it; I'm quite proud of it. I think to myself that I'm quite unique. I've got a lot of talents and abilities and I think 'Well, so bloody what if I've got epilepsy'. I don't see why it has to have a stigma because as far as I know, people with epilepsy don't harm other people. Maybe it's not nice to look at, but that's what I feel now: I feel tough. I used to be a great worrier of what people thought, but being sick and alone and stuck in bed stopped that. Being sick in a bucket and sitting on a toilet for weeks on end, all alone when all my family and friends disappeared, taught me not to worry about what other people think now. I might still worry a little bit but I feel more confident in going along with how *I* feel; actually being able to say, 'Well I've got this and this is what happens.' I've noticed it's better, the more I talk, the more grounded I am, the better I feel. I'm feeling more centred now as I talk. The epilepsy – to me it's like it's stuff coming out. I feel it's a lot to do with depressed energy at some level, like creative or emotional or mental or whatever. I feel like it's energy trapped and it sort of explodes. That's my feeling.

My sister has similar feelings, but when I told her it might be epilepsy, she didn't quite like it. She said it frightened her. It doesn't scare me. She says 'It's because she's a shitter and I'm not'. She would always run off and I would land up in situations because I would put on a front and take the blame or face up to whoever. She says that's how I'm responding now. However, she says after reading about epilepsy, she's more convinced. She's been told she's got visual spacial vertigo, but after reading about photosensitive epilepsy she said that she now beleives that they've given her all this crap. She said always when she felt a turn coming on, she's had to pull at herself to stop herself passing out and had to lie down. She's always done that. She saw a neurologist donkeys years ago, but nothing was done. She was always going to the doctor with a dead right side, I think. We've always been told by people that we were both odd, funny, mad, strange and we've had some big fights over it; because if you don't know what's happening, if you've got a person whose okay and then they've gone off doing strange things, then it's difficult to deal with. People can't see that you're under attack, when you're doing peculiar things. I know it sounds odd but it's the 'not being quite here' that's scary. I remember thinking, 'Oh my God, am I off my head?' and being overcome with fear. The confusion is a big part of this as well, because I was so confused I couldn't do anything about it.

Knowing I probably have a recognised condition, I feel much more confident because I'm not so scared of it. Also, I don't have such bad turns; now they are quite mild experiences. I'm aware of what it is and I can say to myself 'Just hold on, it's not going to last.' Also the group handed out published information on counter-measures. So now I would instinctively stamp my feet to try and ground myself if I felt as if I was taking off, not physically, but as though I was leaving my body. It happened at the airport when I went to Amsterdam. I know that yoga helps because the doctor at the rehab centre told me to continue with yoga. She said, 'Are you likely to want to take medication for it?' So I said no, because I've been hooked on medication of one form or another all my life so there would be no point. At one point I was trying to suppress it all with migraine pills and the like. So she said that in that case she thought it would be very important to continue with yoga on a regular basis, because one side of the brain races ahead and yoga and meditation bring them into an even keel. I've discovered other things like playing Monopoly or maybe using a bit of my brain that I don't like, such as having to do arithmetic or similar things can affect me. I think woodwork is particularly good. It's calming. I've got a theory that it's good for everybody with epilepsy.

I also heard that if you have epilepsy, one of the best possible diets is one high in fat because there's something in the fat that coats the nerves and helps stop the abnormal transmissions. As far as I know it's vegetable fat that is good for the myelin sheathing around the nerves; so I make a cocktail, sunflower, sesame, olive oil, cold pressed, not refined and I just keep it in a jar in the fridge. That way I get a selection of all the different vegetable oils. I'm sure it helps. When my sister was skint, I would go round there and be pouring olive oil, grapeseed oil over everything and she'd be saying, 'I'm really skint this week'. I'd say, 'If you're so bloody tight I'll buy you one, but I love it.' All kinds of oil – grapeseed oil and any seed oil – are mood lifters as well. The lithium in them is an antidepressant. They give it to people with depressive illnesses. It occurs naturally in the soil. I love finding out all these little bits. I'd like to write a book myself because I've found out all these little bits and I think, 'Bloody hell, why don't they tell you? Why do they dose people up?' I would seriously say that my moods would lift with eating certain foods: seeds and nuts.

My behaviour has changed after finding out about my epilepsy. I've got more cautious, especially after being clonked on the head at the bus stop; I was attacked. I stopped going out in the evenings. Since I've known I've had this people have said to me I shouldn't go swimming alone. In the summer I was in the sea in Greece. There was a really nice German man with a little boy and I said to my sister, 'He was nice'. She said, 'He was giving you a look'. I said, 'I can't be as grotty as I thought'. I was thinking maybe I should ask him to keep an eye on me. Maybe that was why he was looking at me because the next thing I knew I'd disappeared some-where. There was no one in the water and I was way out, and it was very deep. That was really silly because the sun and the reflections must have brought it on. But you see I didn't want to have this epilepsy, I didn't want to be ill any more. I'd had enough of illness and I wanted to be a capable, independent person who could go in the sea. Afterwards I thought that was a very silly thing to do because at the time I didn't know where I'd gone. I wasn't unconscious, but I wasn't there because I didn't see the people go. I must have been out for enough time for them all to go. I can't swim well and it was deep and I was out of it, so that was very stupid. People said not to do that and now I understand why. It was a stupid thing to do, but then what do I do? Do I say to people, 'Will you come and hold my hand when I go swimming because I have mild epilepsy?' That's the trouble with this. Everyone is different. Some of us can go swimming on our own and others can't.

I find when I'm having to concentrate, focus on one thing, the more likely it is to make me go off on a fit. So if I'm in the doctor's and they're sitting there looking, and I have to concentrate and respond to questions, I feel myself going off. The phone, too, is a problem. Sometimes I can't dial. If a fit comes on I go dyslexic. I can't read or dial and I can't write. I get names wrong. I got a fit yesterday when I phoned the beautician because I wanted a facial, and as she was talking I couldn't get a hold on myself. She's very officious anyway, so I don't think she even noticed because that's the way she is; she overrides people. I found her quite in-timidating; she wasn't the person I wanted to speak to. That wasn't a big deal, but those sort of situations – going into a strange place also affects me. I find I'm better with people I know who accept me. That's where I get quite resentful feelings towards people in my family. When I say, 'Would you come with me to the doctor's?' they say, "Oh, you're all right, you've been all round the world. You go in there and stand your ground,' They can't grasp what happens to me internally because they see me as a capable person. They can't grasp what's happening inside.

I sort of shut down in stressful situations. I was attacked by a man in somebody's flat. I'll explain the situation because people have said, 'Why didn't you kick him?' 'Why didn't you do this?' but what they don't understand is the shut-down in the brain. It was all so all so quick and confusing. He locked the door and drew the curtains and I just shut down and I knew I had to get out. It was like a survival instinct. I remember talking absolute dribble and gibberish. I actually got out but I don't know what was in his mind. I don't know if he thought because I was constantly talking that I was willing. I don't think anyone in their right mind could think that. It's those sort of situations that affect me.

It's the same when I got bashed at the bus stop. I think I was having a fit a bit before because I'd been in bed all afternoon, and I got dressed like a robot and went on a walkabout. I went to church and as I was walking I remember thinking, 'My God what a horrible day. Why are all these people flying in the street?' Of course, they weren't, it was me. I was at the bus stop and I got this feeling of foreboding when five men were coming toward me but I couldn't get out of it. My intuition said 'Get away', but I was miles away in my head. The intuition was there but it was the physical thing that stopped me and the next thing I heard was an almighty crash and that was my skull being hit from the back. The physical shock grounded me and I started screaming at them. It sounds odd, but I think the physical bash on the head brought me back down to earth.

My epilepsy really effects my speech and my understanding. If I'm in a supermarket, for example, I might be talking to myself, saying 'Go away you bastards, leave me alone,' and there's no one near me. I think to myself, 'For God's sake, you're off your rocker.' But I know I'm not. I know it's certain situations; it must be the lights in supermarkets. I went to a psychic surgeon about six years ago and I didn't take in a lot of what he said because I was very ill, but the one thing that came back to me was I'd become photosensitive due to my illness. He said I must never look at the sun or direct light. He said I must wear dark glasses all the time, even in winter, never look at the sun and always sit in the shade. He never mentioned epilepsy because he was a very well known healer in Wales and he's very ethical, and they're not allowed to diagnose. It's against the law for them to diagnose but they can give advice, so they say the words according to the law. I remember him saying that I was very ill and it was very important that I mixed with the right people because that had a bearing on my health. That makes sense, because I used to get vibes from people, weird vibes, and people would say that I was paranoid. I'd get a picture that they were mixed up with heroin and I would see them going to a prison, then it turned out they were; they were involved in heroin and here was no way I could have known.

el much more clear about things now. Before, the psychic

not being able to get feedback on my feelings was actually bringing on the fits. It has been good to share all this weirdness with others and find that it isn't so strange after all. I think there's a lot of psychic stuff mixed up with temperal-lobe epilepsy; creative stuff. Getting it out has been wonderful for me.